BLACK'S N

C000200918

MEDICINAL
PLANTS

OF BRITAIN AND EUROPE

Wolfgang Hensel

A&C BLACK
LONDON

Contents

How to Use this Book

For each medicinal plant described in this book you will find details about its natural habitat and interesting facts on its use, history or biology. Clear illustrations pointing out key features make it easy to identify the plant. The main photograph shows the plant's typical appearance or a characteristic image of the flower. Other illustrations highlight further details that are important for correct identification. Text and illustrations in the margin provide additional information about the plant's habitat, key characteristics and a drawing of a typical flower. Some plants are described across a whole page, and in these cases, either a typical recipe for its medicinal use is given in a box entitled 'Health tip', or a particularly interesting fact about the plant species is displayed in a 'Did you know?' box.

Height (H)
average height of plant from ground

Month
main flowering season

Form
Is the plant annual, biennial or perennial? If perennial, is it herbaceous or woody, a tree or a shrub? A symbol indicates if the plant is poisonous.

General Information
This section gives interesting facts about the plant's history and its medicinal use in a variety of different fields, including conventional medicine, folk medicine, herbalism, homeopathy and Bach flower remedies.

Typical Appearance
A large photograph shows the plant as a whole or a relevant part of the plant. Captions highlight particular features.

Box
The 'Health tip' box contains recipes or suggestions for common or particularly effective remedies using this plant, e.g. in herbal teas, tinctures or balms. The 'Did you know?' box contains information on related plant species or interesting facts about the plant's history or medicinal properties.

Vale
Valerian
H 40–100c

An unusu
attractive
times, this
even the p
– and as an
sedative wa
recent rese
application
form, rathe

Health tip
For a soothing bath add 2 litres of water to 100g Valerian roots and bring to a boil. Strain after 10 minutes and add the decoction to your bath water.

Common Name
Scientific Name
Plant Family

lis (valerian family)
_ herbaceous perennial

 of Valerian is that the dried root is very
ho are drawn to it by its scent. In mediaeval
nt was believed to ward off evil spirits and
it was also used to attract the opposite sex
siac. Its now more common use as a natural
vn in those days and is the result of more
rian is a good example for the 'true'
cinal plant: it works best in its original
ourified extracts.

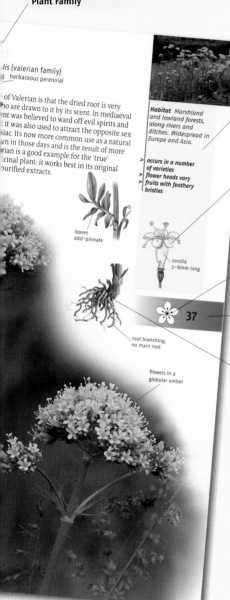

Habitat Marshland and lowland forests, along rivers and ditches. Widespread in Europe and Asia.

> occurs in a number of varieties
> flower heads vary
> fruits with feathery bristles

leaves
odd-pinnate

corolla
3–8mm long

37

root branching,
no main root

flowers in a
globular umbel

Habitat
A photograph shows the plant in one of its natural habitats. The text describes other types of habitat in which it occurs, as well as its distribution in Europe and worldwide.

Key Facts
A short summary of the most relevant information about the plant, e.g. for identification, or about its distribution or use.

Flower
A drawing of a typical flower, highlighting any key characteristics relevant for identification. For composite flowers, a whole flower head is usually shown.

Symbol
The schematic drawing acts as a key for subdivision of the colour-coded sections.

Colour Code
Each of the five main groups is colour-coded according to flower colour (see also page 1).

Identification Details
Small additional illustrations show relevant details of the plant that are significant for correct identification or use as a medicinal plant. These may be illustrations of the leaves, fruits, additional flower details or plant roots. Captions highlight the relevant key features.

Flower Colour

What we see as colour is really just reflected light at different wavelengths, which the eye registers and the brain translates into different colour perceptions. The colour of a flower therefore only becomes 'real' in our mind. Bees, butterflies and bumblebees 'see' quite different colours, as their eyes register different wavelengths than the human eye. Over the course of evolution, flowers have adapted to their pollinators (rather than to our perception of beauty!). For example, ultraviolet light rays are invisible to us, whereas for a bee, ultraviolet spots or stripes on a white flower are like guiding lights pointing the way to the nectar. On the other hand, bees are unable to see the colour red.

Why red is sometimes blue

Light of different wavelengths – i.e. the colour of flowers – is created through pigments within the flower, which absorb parts of the white light rays from the sun and reflect others. One of the most important groups of pigments are anthocyanins. These are water-soluble glucosides found in the plant cell vacuole. Depending on the pH value of the water solution in the cell, anthocyanin pigments reflect either the red or the blue range of the visible light spectrum. This explains why some flowers appear to change colour depending on the acidity of the soil they grow in.

Pale yellow and white shades are created by flavonols and their relatives; deep yellow colours result from the presence of carotenoids, anthoxanthins and betalin pigments. The combination of pigmentation and different surface textures – matt, silky or smooth – creates the vivid array of flower colours that we enjoy in gardens and herbaceous borders.

The Poppy's **bright red** is created by anthocyanin.

The Hawthorn flower reflects all colours of the light spectrum and therefore appears **white**.

Anthocyanins are responsible for the **blue colour** of Flax.

The **yellow colour** pigment in the Broom flower is a carotinoid.

The **green colour** of the Herb Paris flower is due to high chlorophyll levels.

The anthocyanins in Lungwort appear at **first red, then turn blue**.

Typical Flower Shapes

A flower's different elements are grouped into calyx (the sepals), corolla (the petals), stamens and pistil. The stamens represent the male reproductive organ of the plant. They consist of filament and anther, where the pollen is formed. The pistil (or carpel) consists of ovary, style and stigma, the flower's female reproductive parts. Flowers where all of these parts are present are known as 'complete flowers': some flowers have no calyx, or the sepals and petals look identical. Shape and structure of their flowers are a main distinguishing factor of the different plant families. The different parts of a flower tend to be symmetrically arranged, and different flower shapes can be defined according to symmetry and number of petals.

 Flowers with no more than four petals

Cruciform flowers, e.g. White Mustard, have two symmetrical planes.

 Flowers with five petals

The Mallow with **five petals** is radially symmetrical.

Aquilegia with **five fused petals** also has radial symmetry.

 Flowers with more than five petals or composite flowers

Some flowers, such as Hepatica, have **more than five petals.**

Common Chicory has a **composite flower (capitulum) consisting of ray florets.**

The capitulum of the Milk Thistle is composed only of **disc florets.**

The Daisy has a composite flower consisting of **disc and ray florets.**

The Burnet flower consists of **small individual flowers arranged in a dense cluster.**

 Flowers bilaterally symmetrical

The Aconite flower has only **one symmetrical plane.**

All plants of the mint family, such as Stachys, have **labiate flowers.**

The flowers of Broom are characteristic of the **Leguminosae or pea family**.

How Flowers are Arranged on the Stem

Take one glance at a flowering meadow and you will see straight away that few plants are content with just one single flower. A closer look reveals that all the different flowers have their own, very distinctive way of growing on the plant's stem. Indeed, the way the flowers are arranged on the stem is a vital clue in plant identification. In order to clearly identify a plant species, it may help to look closely at the way the flowers are attached in relation to the stem and to the flowers next to them on the same plant.

family. Botanists have a whole host of different specialist terms for these distinct clusters of flowers – or inflorescences – but in this book we only distinguish the most important and characteristic shapes. Where it is necessary to give further detail, descriptive words such as dense, loose, branching, high, etc. will be used.
The previous page showed a composite flower, characteristic of the daisy family.

One flower or many flowers appearing as one?

Few plants have just one solitary flower per individual plant. One example of this is Herb Paris, also known as One Berry. Much more common are single flowers at the top of each shoot, Poppy flowers for example. Composite flowers are different in that what looks like a single flower is actually a flower head composed of many separate unstalked flowers, or 'florets', close together (also known as 'capitulum'). This is typical of the daisy family, e.g. Dandelion.

The Gratiole has **single flowers on long stalks** growing from the leaf axils.

The **umbel** of the Wild Carrot is made up of many individual flower stalks all growing from one point at the end of the stem.

Strength in numbers

Sometimes the individual flowers of a plant are arranged closely together in characteristic clusters. These clusters are often clearly recognisable even from afar, and can help in identifying the plant or even an entire plant

A raceme is a slender and elongated flower head, similar to a spike, but with flowers on short stalks. An example is the Liquorice flower.

The flowers of the Deadnettle are arranged in **whorls** around the stem of the plant.

The simple flowers of grasses, for example, Barley, are usually arranged in **panicles or spikes**.

The **catkins** of the Birch tree are pendant flower heads composed of small, densely packed flowers.

The scales of a Cedar **cone** contain the female ovules from which the seeds grow without the protection of a fruit shell.

The Plantain flower is a **spike** consisting of individual, unstalked flowers that sit directly on the stem (sessile).

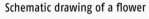

Some medicinal plants are not seed-bearing. Horsetail, for example, reproduces through spores, which grow in a cone-like structure called **strobilus**.

Schematic drawing of a flower

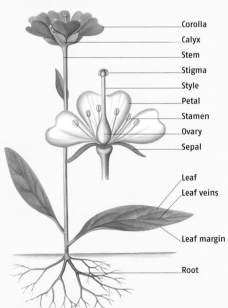

Corolla
Calyx
Stem
Stigma
Style
Petal
Stamen
Ovary
Sepal

Leaf
Leaf veins

Leaf margin

Root

Leaf Shapes and Forms

The leaves of a plant are where the process of photosynthesis takes place. Using sunlight as its source of energy, the chlorophyll in the leaf cells produces sugar from carbon dioxide and water. For this, the shape of the leaves is largely irrelevant – all that matters is maximising the surface area facing towards the sun. Leaf shape and arrangement are, however, species indicators that assist in plant identification. It is therefore helpful to know a little about the most common terms used to describe leaf morphology.

Basic leaf forms

In addition to the shape and form of the leaves themselves, the leaf margins are also important species indicators. Botanists distinguish very precisely whether the leaf margin is entire, serrate or doubly serrate, serrulate, dentate, crenate or lobate etc. In our plant descriptions we only refer to the leaf margins if they hold essential clues for identification.

A **simple leaf** consists of the leaf stalk (petiole), which may continue as the main leaf vein, and the leaf blade (lamina) (e.g. Moneywort). Compound leaves, on the other hand, consist of any number of leaf blades that can be arranged on the stalk in a number of different ways. Intermediate forms also exist.

Pinnately compound leaves have individual leaflets arranged along the central leaf vein (rachis). Pinnate leaves are further distinguished according to the way the leaflets are arranged: **odd-pinnate** leaves have a leaflet at the top end of the rachis; on **even-pinnate** leaves this is missing (e.g. Silverweed).

If the **individual leaflets** are themselves pinnate, the leaves are described as bi-, or even tripinnate (e.g. Bishop's Weed).

Palmately compound leaves have leaflets radiating from one point at the end of the leaf stalk (e.g. Horse Chestnut).

Leaf shapes

Leaves, as well as leaflets of compound leaves, come in numerous different shapes.

Round, circular or **oval-shaped** leaves (e.g. Alder).

Oval or egg-shaped leaves (e.g. Beech).

Lanceolate or spear-shaped leaves are wider at the base and pointed at the top (e.g. Oleander).

Narrow or linear leaves are significantly longer than they are wide (e.g. Tarragon).

Heart-shaped leaves are easy to recognise (e.g. Garlic Mustard).

Needle-shaped leaves are typical of conifers such as Pine and Spruce.

Scale-shaped leaves grow flat on the stem. On flowering plants they are relatively rare (e.g. Coltsfoot).

Arrangement of leaves on the stem

The way the leaves are attached to the stem of a plant also assists in identification.

The basal leaves of many herbaceous plants often form a characteristic **rosette** (e.g. Daisy, above, or Sempervivum, below).

Alternate leaves are attached singly at the nodes and alternate in direction (e.g. Opium Poppy).

Opposite leaves grow in pairs from each node (e.g. Centaury). Alternate and opposite leaves are useful indicators in identifying tree species.

Whorled leaves are less common. Here several leaves are attached at each node, growing directly on the stem (e.g. Lady's Bedstraw).

The Chemistry of Medicinal Plants

Mallow

 Mucilage The mucilage produced by medicinal plants comes in different chemical compositions, but it always contains sugar molecules that form polymers with plant acids or other substances. A key property of mucilage is that it stores water, which is used for seed germination and as a food reserve. Plants that are rich in mucilage can help relieve constipation and soothe inflammations of the mucous membranes, such as those that cause coughs and sore throats.

Silverweed

 Tannins The name of these complex molecules refers to their use in tanning animal hides into leather. Combined with protein, tannins form insoluble compounds. They react with the surface of skin or mucous membranes, effectively 'sealing' it. This astringent property is put to use in the treatment of wounds and internal bleeding.

Hops

 Bitter agents Bitter agents come in a variety of different chemical compositions, but common to all of them is their bitter taste. This stimulates the gastric glands, triggering increased secretion of saliva, gastric fluids and bile. Bitter agents are therefore used to counteract loss of appetite and improve digestion. They also have antibacterial properties, which help promote intestinal health.

Soapwort

 Saponins Saponins are compounds of sugar and aromatic molecules that dissolve in water to form a soapy froth. The roots of Soapwort have traditionally been used as a detergent. In high concentration, or if they get into the bloodstream, saponins are toxic, as they attack the cell membranes. Plants containing low levels of saponin are used as an expectorant in cough remedies or as a diuretic to flush out the kidneys.

Solidago

Flavonoids Chemically these are a class of poly-phenolic compounds, often in combination with sugar or other molecules. Only certain types of flavonoids are actually yellow as their name suggests (from Latin, flavus = yellow). Depending on their chemical structure, different types of flavonoids have different medicinal properties, from diuretic (Solidago) to toning the blood vessels (Horse Chestnut).

Coltsfoot

Pyrrolizidine alkaloids This particular group of alkaloids is found in a number of different plant species that have in the past been used in medicines. However, recent research has shown that pyrrolizidine alkaloids can damage the liver, and may even cause cancer. In some instances, such as Coltsfoot, alkaloid-free varieties are now being grown. However, you may wish to avoid herbal teas made from Coltsfoot, Butterbur, Comfrey, Alkanet and a number of other herbs.

Deadly Nightshade

Alkaloids These are organic compounds containing nitrogen in a variety of different combinations. There are more than 7,000 known alkaloids. Many of the most poisonous plant substances are alkaloids, including nicotine, morphine, strychnine, the atropine in Deadly Nightshade and the aconitine in Monkshood. These plants or substances must never be used for self-medication but only if prescribed by a qualified medical practitioner.

Foxglove

Cardiac glycosides These are also referred to as Digitalis glycosides, since the substance was first discovered in Foxglove (*Digitalis*). There are a number of different molecular forms, but all of them are based on a combination of steroids and sugar – in chemistry, glyco stands for sugar molecules. Cardiac glycosides stimulate the heart muscle and are prescribed for congestive heart failure.

Application of Medicinal Plants

This book is, of course, no substitute for visiting your GP or medical practitioner, or consulting a pharmacist or naturopath. However, it is hoped that the book will inspire you to find out more about the beneficial plants around you, in gardens, parks and in nature.

Collecting medicinal plants

Not so long ago, it was still relatively easy to go out and gather medicinal herbs in the wild. But, sadly, this is no longer the case. Few people now live in places where herbs can simply be picked where they grow. Dust and pollution mean that many plants growing in the wild are contaminated and no longer good for medicinal use. In addition, many plants are protected by law or, in certain areas, bylaws may prohibit picking any wild plants at all.

If plants have been collected, they need to be dried thoroughly, or they may go mouldy, and then stored in light-proof glass jars, ceramic containers or tins.

All the various problems associated with collecting and storing your own herbal remedies can be avoided by buying ready-prepared herbs. These will have been grown or collected under controlled conditions and are subject to quality control standards. A qualified herbalist will also be able to advise on the correct dosage and preparation of your herbal remedy and can warn you about possible side effects and contraindications – whether there are any health conditions where it may be better to avoid this particular herb.

Try a cup of herbal tea

Most herbal remedies are taken in the form of herbal tea. The leaves and flowers, sometimes also parts of the fruit, are prepared as a herbal infusion. Place the dried herbs in a jug and add fresh boiling water. (Use a measuring cup to work out the capacity of your teacup – unless otherwise stated the recipes in this book are based on a

Camomile

150ml cup.) Cover the jug with a saucer while leaving it to infuse and strain the tea through a sieve before drinking. For a decoction, for instance of crushed bilberries, the fruit is boiled briefly in water and then left to stand for a while before straining. Plants that are rich in mucilage, such as Marsh Mallow root, should be soaked in cold water for several hours (cold infusion) and are warmed through just before drinking.

Take a deep breath

Certain plant oils or herbs containing essential oils are more effective if absorbed through the nostrils. For a steam inhalation, add a few drops of essential oil, for instance Spruce oil, to a bowl of steaming hot water, lean over the bowl and cover your head with a towel. Breathe deeply. Then dry your face and rest. For partial baths, such as a footbath of Walnut leaves, prepare the plant parts as an infusion or decoction and then pour this into a large bowl. For an immersion bath, for example with Lavender or Valerian, prepare the herbs with a small amount of water first – usually as a herbal infusion – and then add this to your bath water.

Wraps, compresses and rinses

Other herbal applications are all based on the same preparations already described. A gargle uses a herbal infusion, only in this case it is not swallowed but spat out again. Rinses are prepared like partial baths; and for compresses, a clean cloth or kitchen towel is soaked in the herbal preparation.

Spruce

Blackberry

Heather

Calluna vulgaris (heather family)

H 30–100cm   Aug–Oct   dwarf shrub

Habitat *Moor, heath and rough grassland, bogs, pine forests. On nutrient-poor, acidic soils. Europe to Asia Minor.*

> *flowers in one-sided racemes*
> *sepals similar to petals, but twice as long*

sepals fused at base

When the Heather is in bloom, a plant is blossoming whose medicinal powers have been known since mediaeval times. These days, however, Heather is used only in folk medicine and in homeopathy. The leaves and flowers contain tannins, flavonoids and plant acids. A herbal tea made from Heather acts as a diuretic for bladder and kidney complaints and is said to relieve insomnia and rheumatism. In Bach flower remedies, Heather is credited with helping to improve personal relationships.

18

4 sepals and 4 petals

leaves evergreen, surrounding woody stalk in four rows

Health tip

Heather flower tea with honey as a natural sleep aid: use 1 tsp of flowers per cup, add boiling water and leave to infuse for 10 minutes. Strain, sweeten with honey and sip slowly while hot.

Daphne

Daphne mezereum (daphne family)
H 40–120cm   March–April   shrub

leaves emerge
at tip of each
shoot

Daphne is an extremely poisonous plant and must under no circumstances be used for self-medication. In former times, herbalists used extracts from the plant's bark and berries as a purgative and to treat blisters, rheumatism, gout and even whooping cough. Today the green bark is used in homeopathy for skin conditions, digestive disorders and rheumatic complaints.

red berries
(drupes),
5–10mm in
diameter

Habitat Mixed deciduous forests with dense undergrowth. On nutrient-rich, alkaline soils. Europe to western Asia.

> deciduous, lanceolate leaves
> sepals only, no petals
> leaves emerge after flowering

sepals
covered
in silky
hairs

19

Rosebay Willowherb

Epilobium angustifolium (willowherb family)
H 60–120cm   July–Aug   herbaceous perennial

The brightly coloured flowers of Rosebay Willowherb make it a very noticeable plant when in bloom. The green parts are dried and contain a combination of active elements, which can help relieve the symptoms of benign prostate enlargement. In folk medicine, Rosebay Willowherb was used as a remedy for stomach and digestive complaints and to heal wounds. In eastern Europe the young leaves are used in a popular tisane known as 'Kaporie tea'.

Habitat Clearings and woodland glades, along road verges. Forms dense, conspicuous colonies. Europe, Asia, North America.

> flower changes from male to female
> colonising plant with a profusion of wind-borne seeds

mature flowers
symmetrical

seeds released
all at once

long pod-like
fruit capsules

Small-flowered Willowherb
Epilobium parviflorum (willowherb family)
H 30–80cm   June–Sept   herbaceous perennial

Habitat *Along streams and damp paths, in ditches and in all moist, nutrient-rich soils. Widespread in Europe, Asia and northern Africa.*

> **leaves opposite, not clasping, upper leaves alternate**
> **round stem, densely covered in spreading hairs**

heart-shaped petals, 6–9mm across

As the English name suggests, the Small-flowered Willowherb does not sport spectacular blossoms. Nevertheless, this more modest representative of the willowherb genus has the same medicinal powers as its large-flowered relative. The herb is collected while in flower and contains flavonoids and tannins. Its ability to improve urine flow has been scientifically proven. Its alleged powers as a cure for prostate cancer, however, remain without evidence.

flowers emerge from axils of upper leaves

fruit capsule splits open

extremely hairy seeds

Health tip

Willowherb tea (can also be made with Rosebay Willowherb): add boiling water to 2 tsp of the herb. Leave to infuse for 15 minutes, then strain. This tea should not be consumed over extended periods of time.

Henna Plant

Lawsonia inermis (loosestrife family)
H 2–6m   Oct–April   shrub

petals with
ruffled edges

In Arabic countries, Henna was already well known as a medicinal plant long before it became popular in the western world as a natural hair dye. The dye in the leaves of the plant was used as a remedy for diarrhoea (amoebic dysentery), stomach ulcers and fever. Externally, a decoction from the leaves was used to treat eczema, ulcers, fungal infections and scabies.

leaves oval,
pointed

Habitat *Dry, arid regions. North Africa as far as the Sahara desert, India.*

> bark pale, almost white
> flowers in panicles, ranging from white to red

solitary
flower

Corn Poppy

Papaver rhoeas (poppy family)
H 30–90cm   May–July   annual

The bright red petals contain no pharmaceutically active chemicals. However, despite its relatively low alkaloid levels, Poppy tea has been used in folk medicine for pain relief and to treat insomnia. Poppy syrup is taken as a cough remedy and for sore throats and hoarseness. The leaves are commonly added to other herbal teas to improve their colour.

fruit capsule
cylindrical with
a rounded
base

deflexed
flower bud

Habitat *Cornfields, waysides, wasteland sites and disturbed ground. On nutrient-rich, alkaline soils. Worldwide.*

> flower bud deflexed, flower and fruit upright
> flower bright red with dark centre
> milky white sap

stigma with
8–18 rays

Opium Poppy

Papaver somniferum (poppy family)

H 40–150cm   June–Aug   annual   ☠

Habitat *Wasteland, rubble. On rich loamy soils. Native to western Asia. Cultivated legally as well as illegally.*

> **leaves irregularly toothed, clasping the stem**
> **single flowers, up to 10cm large**
> **white milky sap**

The Opium Poppy shows poignantly how a drug can be both a blessing and a curse. If you score the young fruit capsules of an Opium Poppy, a milky sap emerges, which dries and hardens on contact with the air. This resin contains over 40 different alkaloids, which are processed into a wide range of pharmaceutical substances – morphine, codeine, noscapine and papaverine being the most widely known. On the other hand, opium and its derivatives (e.g. heroin) are also strong narcotics with a powerful addictive potential.

fruit capsule rounded, 5–12 stigma rays

seeds of Opium Poppy are edible and non-toxic

petals red to purple

base of petals dark purple

leaves clasping the stem

Did you know?

Babies used to be given a decoction made from poppy capsules as a sedative. However, it's best to steer clear of using this plant unless you know what you're doing! The black poppy seeds used in bakery products, on the other hand, contain none of the dangerous alkaloids and are perfectly safe to enjoy.

Psyllium
Plantago ovata (plantain family)
H 5–20cm   Dec–April   annual to biennial

The special feature of Psyllium is its seed husk. These contain large amounts of mucilage, designed to supply the germinating seed with sufficient water. The seeds, consumed with plenty of water, act as a laxative and digestive stimulant.

Habitat *Dry, exposed ground on sandy soils. Mediterranean region to south-western Asia, Canary Islands.*

> *leaves in a basal rosette*
> *narrow, linear leaves*
> *individual flowers inconspicuous*

flower head

leaves hoary

flowers in round clusters

individual flower pinkish-white

Great Burnet
Sanguisorba officinalis (rose family)
H 30–150cm   June–Sept   herbaceous perennial

Throughout history, Great Burnet has been used as a vulnerary and to stem internal bleeding. This is reflected in the plant's genus name: sanguis, blood, and sorbeo, to staunch. Responsible for this astringent action are the plant's high tannin levels. These days, the plant is prescribed primarily in homeopathy as a remedy for diarrhoea and varicose veins.

Habitat *Wetland meadows and on boggy ground. In nutrient-rich soils up to medium altitudes. Central Europe, Asia, North America.*

> *basal leaves in a rosette*
> *leaves on stem alternate, odd-pinnate*

stigma rounded

spherical flower head, round to oval

individual flower formed from sepals only

Marsh Mallow
Althaea officinalis (mallow family)
H 60–120cm   July–Sept   herbaceous perennial

Habitat *Moist ground, salt marshes, on loamy soils. Asia, eastern Europe, coastal areas.*

> *escapees from gardens often found in the wild*
> *entire plant is covered in a soft down*
> *outer sepals joined at base, petals lobed at the top*

flower 3–5cm across

Marsh Mallow has been used as a medicinal plant since antiquity and is still an accepted remedy in herbal medicine today. A tea made from its leaves, flowers or roots helps alleviate oral and throat infections as well as gastro-intestinal complaints. The plant may even have immune-boosting properties. Marsh Mallow tea with honey is a popular cough remedy and Marsh Mallow poultices are applied in folk medicine for a variety of skin conditions.

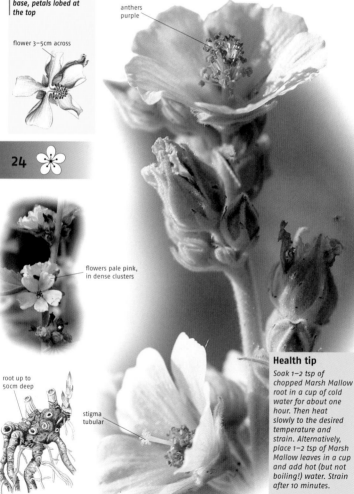

anthers purple

flowers pale pink, in dense clusters

root up to 50cm deep

stigma tubular

Health tip

Soak 1–2 tsp of chopped Marsh Mallow root in a cup of cold water for about one hour. Then heat slowly to the desired temperature and strain. Alternatively, place 1–2 tsp of Marsh Mallow leaves in a cup and add hot (but not boiling!) water. Strain after 10 minutes.

Scarlet Pimpernel

Anagallis arvensis (primrose family)

H 5–30m   June–Oct   annual

blue-flowering

In Greek antiquity this plant was employed as a cure for melancholia and in mediaeval times it was used to treat insanity. In folk medicine the herb is known as a remedy for coughs, liver and kidney complaints, and is applied externally to relieve joint pain. Modern herbal medicine no longer makes use of the Scarlet Pimpernel, although it is occasionally prescribed in homeopathy.

Habitat Gardens and arable fields, along waysides, vineyards, wasteland and disturbed ground. On nutrient-rich, loamy soils. Occurs virtually worldwide.

leaves opposite, sessile

> angular stalk, creeping
> flower bright red to pink or, rarely, blue

petals 3.5–6mm long

petals round to oval

Strawberry Tree

Arbutus unedo (heather family)

H 1.50–6m   Oct–March   small tree

The fruits of this tree resemble strawberries, but are best not eaten raw. The Strawberry Tree is part of the heather family, which also includes the Blueberry. Its leaves contain arbutin, which breaks down into a substance with antiseptic properties. This is used to treat infections of the urinary tract and for benign prostate enlargement. As a tea, the leaves are also used for diarrhoea and as a gargle for oral infections, mouth ulcers and sore throats.

Habitat Mediterranean coastal areas, maquis, evergreen forests.

> leaves evergreen, similar to Bay leaves
> round fruits, resembling strawberries
> flowers white to pink

bell-shaped flowers

round fruits, up to 2cm in diameter

berries with a hard, scaly shell

Deadly Nightshade
Atropa belladonna (nightshade family)
H 50–150cm   June–Aug   herbaceous perennial   🕸

Habitat *Woodland glades and clearings, along waysides. Central Europe, south-western Asia, northern Africa.*

> leaves oval to lanceolate, alternate
> upper leaves (near flower) appear opposite, with one leaf larger than the other

This extremely poisonous plant contains a number of alkaloids (including hyoscyamine), tannins and flavonoids. Another substance, atropine, forms when the plant is dried. Due to its high toxicity, the plant has been little used in folk medicine but was of greater significance in folklore and witchcraft. Modern medicine utilises the plant's active components in standard preparations as an antispasmodic, to reduce excessive secretion of mucous, and in eye drops to dilate pupils for eye examinations.

berries first green, then shiny black

single flowers, pendent, bell-shaped

Did you know?
In Greek mythology, Atropos, one of the Three Fates, holds the shears to cut the thread of life – hence the plant's scientific name. The Scots knew how to use the plant's deadly effect to their advantage: in 1035 they warded off a Viking attack by adding deadly nightshade to the food consumed by the invaders. The alkaloids contained in the plant cause hallucinations.

Common Bistort

Bistorta officinalis ssp. *officinalis* (knotweed family)
H 30–100cm   May–July   herbaceous perennial

The tuberous root is rich in starch and used to be eaten as a vegetable in places like Russia. More important from a medicinal point of view are the tannins, which have an astringent action. The herb is applied externally to treat wounds (in wraps and poultices or herbal baths), but also as a gargle for oral infections and as a tea for diarrhoea.

flowers in dense, cylindrical spikes, 3–6 cm long

basal leaves on long stalks

stamens protruding from corolla

Habitat *Damp meadows and wetlands, near water. In nutrient-rich soils. Central Europe and Asia.*

> *leaves up to 20cm long, lanceolate to spear-shaped*
> *upper leaves sessile*

🌸 27

Cretan Rock Rose

Cistus creticus ssp. *creticus* (rock-rose family)
H 30–100cm   April–June   shrub

The dried resin from this shrub has been known since antiquity under the name 'labdanum'. It was used in cosmetics, as incense and to stem bleeding. These days, the leaves are used to make a herbal tea. They contain polyphenols, which are said to have strong antioxidant properties, and the plant is therefore credited with boosting the immune system and improving overall well-being.

hairy leaves to protect against intense sunshine and heat

profusion of stamens

petals appear creased

Habitat *Dry, rocky ground in full sun. Maquis and garigue (low scrubland). Mediterranean regions.*

> *evergreen*
> *leaves oval to lanceolate, hairy*
> *petals silky, like fine tissue paper*

flowers 4–6cm across

Common Centaury

Centaurium erythraea (gentian family)

H 10–50cm   July–Sept   annual

Habitat *Woodland glades, dry grassland, in dry and sunny locations. Europe, western Asia, northern Africa.*

> *flowers in umbel-like clusters*
> *leaves in a basal rosette*
> *stem angular*

This pretty meadow plant is particularly rich in bitter agents, which are responsible for the distinctive taste common to all preparations of this herb. A tea made from Common Centaury stimulates the gastric glands, relieves bloating and aids digestion. In folk medicine it was used as a treatment for anaemia and intestinal worms. In Bach flower remedies the plant is credited with boosting self-confidence.

petals fused at base forming a tube

top ends of petals 5–8mm long

leaves on stalk opposite

Health tip

Century herbal tonic, to be taken as an aperitif before meals: Pour 1 litre of dry white wine into a jug with 30g each of dried Century leaves and Peppermint leaves. Add the juice of one lemon (or orange). Leave for 7–10 days and then filter through a muslin cloth.

Cyclamen

Cyclamen purpurascens (primrose family)
H 5–15cm   June–Sept   herbaceous perennial 🕱

The tuberous roots of this plant can cause vomiting and diarrhoea with spasms and even paralysis. In folk medicine they were therefore used as a strong purgative. These days, Cyclamen is mainly used in homeopathy, where it is prescribed for headaches, migraines and digestive complaints. In antiquity, Cyclamen was recommended, despite its dangerous side effects, as a cure for a wide variety of ailments, from eye diseases to gout and snakebite.

Habitat *Forests, parks and gardens. Alpine regions.*

> *leaves evergreen, with marbled pattern*
> *available in many varieties as a garden plant*

flowers on fleshy leafless stalks

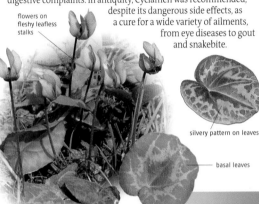

silvery pattern on leaves

basal leaves

flowers deflexed, with upward-pointing lobes

Herb Robert

Geranium robertianum (geranium family)
H 20–40cm   May–Oct   annual

Historic herbals are full of praise for this herb, although these days it is no longer used much apart from, perhaps, in homeopathy. The flowers and green parts are rich in tannins and were taken as a remedy for diarrhoea or applied to slow-healing wounds. In folk medicine the herb was recommended for stomach and digestive complaints and for kidney and bladder infections.

Habitat *Forests, waste ground and rubble, a common weed on walls and in gardens. Central Europe, Asia, northern Africa and North America.*

> *plant has a distinct, slightly pungent smell*
> *leaves deeply lobed*
> *leaves and stalks often have a red tint*

petals 5–12mm long

style

fruit with characteristic 'cranesbill'

flower with vertical stripes

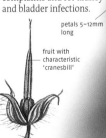

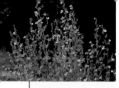

Common Mallow
Malva sylvestris (mallow family)
H 30–100cm   June–Oct   herbaceous perennial

Habitat *Along way-sides, on rubble and waste ground. In dry and sunny locations. Europe, Asia, northern Africa.*

> *grows in nitrogen-rich soils*
> *flowers in clusters of 2 to 6 in upper leaf axils*
> *stem prostrate or decumbent*

petals with dark veins

30

The leaves and especially the flowers of Common Mallow are rich in mucilage, but also contain tannins and flavonoids. The mucilage has a soothing effect on inflamed mucous membranes, which makes Mallow tea an effective remedy for coughs and catarrhs, stomach pain and infections of the digestive system. The flowers give a nice red tint to the tea and are therefore often added to other herbal teas to improve their colour. In former times, Mallow leaves were given as a vegetable to relieve constipation.

petals 20–25mm long

filaments fused into a tube

leaves palmately lobed

Health tip
Add boiling water to 2 tsp per cup of dried Mallow flowers. Leave to infuse for 10–15 minutes, then strain. Alternatively, use a slightly larger amount of flowers for a cold infusion: add cold water and leave for 2–3 hours before straining. Then slowly warm through to the desired temperature.

Oleander

Nerium oleander (dogbane family)
H 1–4m July–Sept shrub ☠

We mainly know Oleander as an ornamental garden plant. In its Mediterranean home and in Arabic medicine, however, the plant has been known since antiquity as an antidote for snakebites. Nowadays, Oleander leaves are used only occasionally and in preparation. They contain cardiac glycosides, which are prescribed for congestive heart failure.

Habitat *Periodically dry streams and river-banks. Mediterranean regions.*

> *in central and northern Europe grown as an ornamental shrub or house plant*
> *evergreen leaves*
> *plant contains a milky sap*

leathery, lanceolate leaves

petals appear twisted

✿ 31

Sweet Almond Tree

Prunus dulcis var. *dulcis* (rose family)
H 2–8m Feb–April tree or shrub

The sweet-tasting seeds are used to produce a valuable oil, which forms the base of creams and massage oils (balms). In folk medicine it was prescribed for stomach and digestive complaints. The residue from almond oil production is used in cleansing face masks. The oil of the closely related Bitter Almond (var. *amara*) is an essential ingredient in the production of fine marzipans.

Habitat *Native to south-western Asia. Cultivated as a crop or ornamental tree in regions with temperate climate.*

> *related Bitter Almond is poisonous*
> *flowers emerge before leaves*
> *leaves lanceolate, finely toothed*

almond

fruit splits open

flowers white to pink

petals lobed at the top

Lungwort
Pulmonaria officinalis (borage family)
H 10–30cm   March–May   herbaceous perennial

Habitat Deciduous forests and shrubland. Throughout Europe.

> plant covered in tiny coarse hairs, feels rough to the touch
> basal leaves on long stalks
> P. obscura *is similar, but without speckled leaves*

Lungwort formerly had a place in almost every garden, for its reputed medical qualities for diseases of the lungs. Its speckled leaves were thought to resemble lung tissue, and their use in former days was partly founded on the 'Doctrine of Signatures', whereby plants were used to treat diseases of those parts of the body they resembled. The leaves contain mucilage and high levels of silicic acid. Lungwort is now only used in homoeopathy in the treatment of bronchitis and in folk medicine for oral and throat infections.

leaves opposite, sessile

Health tip

A herbal infusion to be used as a gargle for coughs and laryngitis: use 1 tsp of dried lungwort leaves per cup, add boiling water and leave to infuse for 10 minutes, then strain. Use as a gargle only – do not swallow.

flowers initially pink, then turn purple to blue

corolla 8–22mm long

leaves with white specks

Rusty-leaved Alpenrose
Rhododendron ferrugineum (heather family)
H 30–120cm   June–Aug   shrub

In Alpine regions, the leaves of the Alpenrose were used as a remedy for rheumatism, gout, migraines and high blood pressure. However, modern herbalists advise against tea made from its leaves, as not all active components of the plant are fully understood. A homeopathic preparation of the leaves and young shoots is prescribed for nerve pain, rheumatic complaints and testicular infections.

Habitat Alps, Pyrenees. Forest margins, shrubland, just above the tree line.

> low, branching shrub
> leaves evergreen, leathery
> rust-coloured glands on underside of leaves

edges of petals curled in

individual flower 25–30mm in diameter

flowers in globular umbels

33

Dog Rose
Rosa canina (rose family)
H 1–3m   June   shrub

Rose hips are especially rich in vitamin C. The shells (with the seeds removed) can be made into tasty jams or dried and added to immune-boosting teas. The entire fruit is utilised for medicinal purposes. Oil from the seeds is used in the treatment of scar tissue and in anti-wrinkle creams. In Bach flower remedies, Dog Rose is said to counteract apathy and resignation.

Habitat Hedgerows, forest margins, waste ground, along roads and waysides. Europe to central Asia.

> thorny branches, climbing or arching
> thorns crescent-shaped with a broad base

petals white to blushed pink

leaves odd-pinnate

fruit (rosehip) bright red, oval

flowers up to 5cm in diameter

Soapwort

Saponaria officinalis (pink family)

H 30–80cm   June–Sept   herbaceous perennial

Habitat Wetlands and floodplains, waste ground, along waysides. On nutrient-rich soils. Widespread in southern and central Europe.

> pure white varieties occur
> leaves lanceolate with three leaf veins

Soapwort root contains up to 8% saponins as well as carbohydrates and various other substances. Its application as a medicinal plant dates back to antiquity when Arabic physicians used it to treat skin diseases such as psoriasis, boils and ulcers, and even leprosy. Mediaeval herbalists used the root for its expectorant qualities as a remedy for coughs and respiratory infections. In folk medicine Soapwort was used to relieve skin conditions and rheumatic complaints.

root used for medicinal purposes

petals 10–15mm long

sepals fused, 20–25mm long

flowers in loose umbels

Did you know?

The name 'Soapwort' refers to another former use of the plant: when dissolved in water, saponins form a soapy froth. The root was therefore used chiefly as a detergent, rather than for its medicinal properties.

Scopolia
Scopolia carniolica (nightshade family)
H 20–60cm   April–May   herbaceous perennial   ☠

This plant is named after Antonio Scopoli (1723–88), who described it in his *Flora of Slovenia*. There, it was considered an aphrodisiac and a witches' herb – it contains hallucinogenic alkaloids. As a medicinal plant it has been used for its antispasmodic properties. However, it is now rarely used for this purpose, as other, more effective remedies are available. In folk medicine it was used in the treatment of rheumatism, gout and toothache.

Habitat *Undergrowth of deciduous forests. South-eastern Europe.*

> **leaves lanceolate, with pointed tips and narrowing towards the stalk**
> **single flowers, nodding**
> **flowers purple outside, yellowish-green inside**

tubular, bell-shaped flowers

leaves shiny

flowers nodding

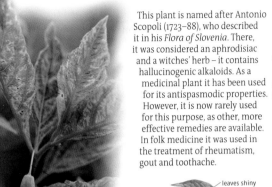

35

Common Comfrey
Symphytum officinale ssp. *officinale* (borage family)
H 30–100cm   May–July   herbaceous perennial   ☠

The belief that Comfrey can heal broken bones seems to be as old as herbal medicine itself. It goes back to antiquity and is reflected in the plant's scientific name (from Greek sympho = to unite) as well as several of the plant's older English names such as Knitbone or Bruisewort. The root contains saponins, tannins and mucilage. However, it also contains pyrrolizidine alkaloids, which have been linked to cancer, and the herb is therefore now only used externally.

Habitat *Near water, along waysides, meadows and lowland forests. On moist, nutrient-rich soils. Europe, Asia.*

> **entire plant covered in bristly hairs**
> **flower buds curled inwards**
> **flower colour ranges from yellowish-white to purple and violet**

leaves decurrent (base of the leaf runs down the stem)

corolla 10–20mm long

flowers nodding

Bilberry
Vaccinium myrtillus (heather family)
H 15–50cm   April–Aug   dwarf shrub

Habitat *Mixed and coniferous forests, dry upland heaths and moors. Acidic, nutrient-poor soils. Europe, north-western Asia.*

> **green stem with sharp edges or wings**
> **leaves deciduous, ovate, alternate**

The Bilberry is a close relative of the Blueberry, whose fruits have become a popular 'superfood', and has been known as a medicinal plant for centuries. The berries contain high levels of tannin and, although fresh bilberries can cause diarrhoea if consumed in large quantities, the dried berries act as a remedy for it. Freshly pressed diluted bilberry juice soothes oral and throat infections and a tea made from the leaves is a household remedy for stomach and digestive complaints and bladder weakness. Its alleged ability to lower blood sugar levels has not been scientifically proven.

flower globular with 4–5 lobes

berries with remnants of corolla

corolla spherical, 4–7mm long

Health tip

As a remedy for diarrhoea, use 1–2 tbsp of dried bilberries per cup, add cold water and bring to boil. Strain after 10 minutes. Leave to cool before drinking.

Valerian

Valeriana officinalis (valerian family)
H 40–100cm   May–Aug   herbaceous perennial

An unusual feature of Valerian is that the dried root is very attractive to cats, who are drawn to it by its scent. In mediaeval times, this same scent was believed to ward off evil spirits and even the plague, but it was also used to attract the opposite sex – and as an aphrodisiac. Its now more common use as a natural sedative was unknown in those days and is the result of more recent research. Valerian is a good example for the 'true' application of a medicinal plant: it works best in its original form, rather than in purified extracts.

Habitat Marshland and lowland forests, along rivers and ditches. Widespread in Europe and Asia.

> occurs in a number of varieties
> flower heads vary
> fruits with feathery bristles

corolla 3–8mm long

leaves odd-pinnate

root branching, no main root

37

flowers in a globular umbel

Health tip

For a soothing bath add 2 litres of water to 100g Valerian roots and bring to a boil. Strain after 10 minutes and add the decoction to your bath water.

Great Burdock

Arctium lappa (daisy family)
H 80–150cm   July–Aug   biennial

Habitat Wasteland, along waysides, fences, railway lines and riverbanks. On nutrient-rich soils. Europe, Asia.

> root can be eaten as a vegetable
> disc florets only
> basal leaves up to 50cm long

Great Burdock root contains mucilage, up to 70% inulin – a type of sugar – and essential oils, together with other substances. Although not used in conventional medicine, Great Burdock has long played an important role in folk medicine as a diuretic, diaphoretic and depurative herb. In wraps and poultices it was applied to slow-healing wounds and eczema and to relieve rheumatic pain. Its active elements have been shown to have antibiotic properties.

profusion of disc florets

purple disc florets

hooked bracts

root is used for medicinal purposes

long-stalked flower head

Autumn Crocus

Colchicum autumnale (autumn crocus family)
H 5–40cm   Aug–Nov   bulb ☠

fruit capsule appears together with leaves

Habitat Damp meadows and orchards. On nutrient-rich soils. Central Europe, northern Africa.

> grazing animals avoid the poisonous plant
> ovary remains protected below ground
> leaves appear in the second year after flowering

flowers very similar to Crocus (but appear in autumn)

The Autumn Crocus contains a lethal poison and has therefore never played a role in folk medicine. However, physicians in historical times knew about the plant's toxicity as well as its other properties, and recommended it as a cure for acute cases of gout. And indeed, colchicine – as the substance is known – is still an approved treatment for this condition today.

petals 4–6cm long

lower part of petals fused into a tube

Purple Coneflower

Echinacea purpurea (daisy family)

H 60–180cm   July–Sept   herbaceous perennial

For its pretty pink flowers, the Purple Coneflower has been a popular ornamental plant since the 18th century, and numerous sub-species and garden varieties are available. North-American Indians used the roots and leaves of the plant as a vulnerary. Although established over recent years as one of the most widely known immune-boosting herbal supplements, the medical profession has now raised some doubts as to Echinacea's usefulness and recommends a more targeted approach.

Habitat *Native to North America, in Europe cultivated as an ornamental and medicinal plant (including large-scale plantations).*

> **leaves narrow, rounded at base**
> **ray florets initially horizontal, curving downwards on older flowers**

disc florets domed

39

ray florets 2–4cm long

leaves ovate with pointed tip and rough surface

Health tip

Not all of the numerous Echinacea supplements keep what they promise. The herb has been proven to be at its most effective if used in the early stages of a cold: taken at the right time, it boosts the body's own immune defences and thus helps to nip the infection in the bud.

Hemp Agrimony
Eupatorium cannabinum (daisy family)
H 50–150cm   July–Sept   herbaceous perennial

Habitat Woodland glades and forest edges. In moist ground, near water. Europe, western Asia, northern Africa.

> leaves opposite, deeply lobed
> also known as 'Holy Rope', because of its similarity to Hemp

flower head in dense umbel-like panicles

flower head with just 4–6 disc florets

perianth 4–6mm long

Physicians used to recommend Hemp Agrimony as an antidote to snakebites and a remedy for dysentery and diseases of the liver. In mediaeval times it was thought to improve sexual prowess. In folk medicine the herb was used to stimulate bile flow and as a diuretic and laxative. The plant's active elements suggest immune-boosting properties. Nevertheless, it plays no significant role in modern medicine.

leaves palmate, in 3–5 lobes

40 ✺

Purple Gentian
Gentiana purpurea (gentian family)
H 20–60cm   July–Sept   herbaceous perennial

Habitat Meadows and pastures, above the tree line, in thin conifer woodland. On lime-free, nutrient-poor soils. Alps, Apennines, Scandinavia.

> leaves opposite
> sepals in 2 lobes, petals fused, 5–8 lobes

corolla 2.5–4cm long

The root of Purple Gentian, like that of its yellow-flowering cousin, contains bitter-tasting glycosides and sugars. In Alpine regions it is used to make schnapps and liqueurs. The distilling process eliminates most of the bitter agents and the resulting drink, known as 'mountain gentian spirit', is said to aid digestion, especially after a rich meal. In Bach flower remedies, Purple Gentian is used to help overcome discouragement and despondency.

flowers at top of stem, in a dense cluster

leaves with 5–7 veins

Purple Loosestrife
Lythrum salicaria (loosestrife family)
H 50–100cm   July–Sept   herbaceous perennial

The dried flowering herb contains tannins, flavonoids and essential oils. Like many herbs that contain tannins it was used in the past to stem bleeding, with applications ranging from heavy periods to external use, e.g. on eczema and leg ulcers. In addition, the herb was known for centuries as a remedy for diarrhoea and dysentery, even typhoid fever. However, modern herbalists no longer make much use of Purple Loosestrife.

Habitat Fens and marshes, ditches, near ponds. On moist and wet ground. Europe, Asia, northern Africa.

> *leaves opposite or in whorls*
> *stem square, angular*
> *length of style and stamens varies*

stamens

style

section through flower showing depth of calyx

flowers in a long spike

individual flower ca. 1cm long

41

Did you know?
The 17th century British herbalist Nicholas Culpeper recommends distilled water ffrom the herb to treat eye problems. writing in his Complete Herbal 'Neither do I know a better pre-server of the sight when it is well, nor a better cure for sore eyes than this used outwardly.

Common Peony
Paeonia officinalis ssp. *officinalis* (peony family)
H 30–120cm   May–June   herbaceous perennial

Common Peony petals contain tannins and colour pigments, which, added to other herbal teas, give them a richer colour. In folk medicine, a tea from Common Peony leaves was used as a remedy for epilepsy, gout and digestive disorders. In Chinese medicine, the root of the related *P. lactiflora* is added to the traditional 'Four Things Soup', a widely used women's tonic in China.

profusion of stamens

style 3-lobed

large flowers, often as double flowers

root is used in Traditional Chinese Medicine

42

Purple Passionflower
Passiflora incarnata (passionflower family)
H 8–10m   climbing   May–July   perennial

The name 'Passionflower' was coined by Christian missionaries who saw in its flower the symbols of the Passion of Christ: the five stamens and three styles symbolise the wounds and the nails, the double row of coloured filaments represents the crown of thorns, the tendrils are the whips and the lobed leaves resemble the clutching hands of the soldiers. The leaves and flowers are sold in herbal preparations and tea mixes to relieve nervous disorders.

corona of fine filaments

flower pink or white, 3–5cm across

5 stamens

3 styles

leaves with 3 deep lobes

Common Butterbur
Petasites hybridus (daisy family)
H 15–150cm   April–May   herbaceous perennial

Butterbur root has been used medicinally since the Middle Ages, when it was wrongly believed to be a cure for the bubonic plague (an older name for the plant is Pestilence Wort). The root contains a number of active chemicals with antispasmodic, anti-inflammatory, and pain-relieving properties. Butterbur root extract was used to treat migraines and tension headaches. However, the wild form contains liver-damaging pyrrolizidine alkaloids. Modern herbal medicine therefore uses preparations made from alkaloid-free varieties.

Habitat *Along rivers and streams, ditches, fens and marshes. On nutrient-rich soils. Europe and western Asia.*

> **flowers emerge before leaves**
> **leaves 90cm wide and (with stalk) up to 150cm tall**

up to 100 capitula on one flower stalk

flower head cylindrical

43

tuberous roots

scale-shaped leaves

Did you know?
The scientific plant name is derived from the Greek word petasos, a wide-brimmed felt hat worn by shepherds, which the Greek physician Dioscorides thought the large leaves of the plant resembled. The plant should not be used for self-medication.

Small Pasque Flower

Pulsatilla pratensis ssp. *pratensis* (buttercup family)
H 200–700cm   April–May   herbaceous perennial   🐝

Habitat *Grassland and open pine forests. On dry, sandy soils. Central and eastern Europe*

> single flowers, nodding
> basal leaves covered in long, shaggy hairs, bi- and tri-pinnate; 3 upper leaves, fused at the nodes

flower deep red to maroon-coloured, usually nodding

Only the fresh herb is poisonous. It was used in folk medicine to treat migraines, skin infections and abdominal cramps. The dried herb was also recommended for digestive disorders and eye diseases. These days it is used primarily in homeopathy, where it is prescribed for a whole range of conditions.

petals covered in white down

corolla up to 2.5cm long

leaves emerge after flowering

44 ❋

Pomegranate

Punica granatum (pomegranate family)
H 2–7m   May–Sept   shrub, small tree

Habitat *Native to south-western Asia; introduced in the Mediterranean.*

> seeds embedded in small, ruby-coloured, fleshy sacs (known as arils)
> leaves opposite, oval, leathery

flower with fleshy calyx

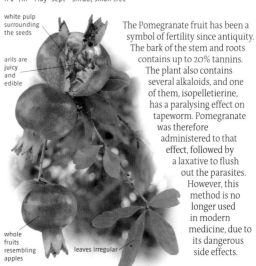

white pulp surrounding the seeds

arils are juicy and edible

whole fruits resembling apples

leaves irregular

The Pomegranate fruit has been a symbol of fertility since antiquity. The bark of the stem and roots contains up to 20% tannins. The plant also contains several alkaloids, and one of them, isopelletierine, has a paralysing effect on tapeworm. Pomegranate was therefore administered to that effect, followed by a laxative to flush out the parasites. However, this method is no longer used in modern medicine, due to its dangerous side effects.

China Rhubarb

Rheum palmatum (knotweed family)

H 100–250cm   May–June   herbaceous perennial

The leaf stalks of rhubarb are well known as a refreshingly tart summer compote or an ingredient in pies and crumbles. The rhubarb species presented here, however, is a different variety of the plant, which is used mainly for medicinal purposes. Its roots contain numerous glycosides, tannins and flavonoids. It is taken as a tea to stimulate the appetite and relieve gastro-intestinal infections. In larger doses it acts as a mild laxative. Homeopathic preparations are prescribed for diarrhoea and given to teething infants.

Habitat Native to China. Introduced to central Europe as an ornamental and medicinal plant.

> flowers with 6 bracts
> large, long-stalked leaves, palmately lobed

flower bracts all the same size

flowers white to pink

flowers in a dense panicle

45

long carrot-shaped root

brown sheath surrounding leaf nodes

Health tip

To relieve constipation: add boiling water to 1/2 tsp per cup of rhubarb root (from a herbalist or health food shop). Infuse for 10–15 minutes, then strain and drink straight away. This tea should only be consumed after consultation with a qualified medical practitioner.

Common Sorrel

Rumex acetosa (knotweed family)

H 30–100cm   May–July   herbaceous perennial

Habitat Meadows and pastures, open ground, weed patches along rivers and streams. On nutrient-rich soils. Northern hemisphere.

> male and female plants
> flowers with 6 outer leaves (bracts), 3 of which become enlarged as the fruit ripens

Although Common Sorrel is not used in conventional medicine, the fresh herb has long been known in folk medicine as a remedy for digestive complaints and infections, and is also used in homeopathy. Its depurative properties have been put to use in fresh salads as part of a spring detox. However, the plant can contain quite high levels of oxalic acid and should therefore not be consumed in large quantities.

flowers in a loose panicle

enlarged inner bracts

flowers in a loose panicle

leaves on long stalks, basal leaves arrow-shaped

leaf sheath

Houseleek

Sempervivum tectorum (stonecrop family)

H 15–50cm   July–Sept   herbaceous perennial

Habitat In dry, rocky places. Alps to Pyrenees. Widely cultivated.

> planted on roofs to protect against lightning
> leaves scale-shaped, flat on the stem
> several flowers emerging at top of stem

The tradition of growing this plant on rooftops goes back to Roman times, and in mediaeval times people believed firmly that Houseleek was a good protection against lightning strikes. The fleshy leaves contain tannins, mucilage and a number of plant acids. The sap of the plant acts cooling and soothing on minor wounds, such as burns or insect bites.

flowers 2–3cm across

12–16 sepals and petals

leaves flat on the stem

main rosette with offshoots

Milk Thistle

Silybum marianum (daisy family)

H 30–150cm   April–Aug   biennial

The name is derived from the milky white markings on the leaves of this plant. In mediaeval times these were seen to symbolise the milk of the Virgin Mary and the plant is also known as 'Our Lady's Thistle'. The flower heads were once considered an effective treatment for depression and the leaves were used for liver and gall bladder complaints. The fruit husks contain a substance known as silymarin, which is used in preparations for acute liver disease and as a preventative supplement for a variety of liver-related problems.

Habitat *Along waysides, on wasteland and disturbed ground. South-western Asia, Mediterranean, cultivated in central Europe.*

> *basal rosette biennial, with clear white markings*
> *flowers appear in year two*

Health tip

To relieve mild digestive complaints: add boiling water to 1 tsp per cup of ground Milk Thistle seeds. Infuse for 10–15 mins, then strain and drink immediately. To improve the taste and further enhance the beneficial effects of the infusion, add a few Peppermint leaves.

spiky bracts surrounding flower

disc florets only

47

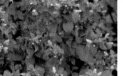

Black Horehound

Ballota nigra (mint family)

H 30–100cm   June–Sept   herbaceous perennial

Habitat *Waysides, wasteland sites, along fences. Common weed on disturbed ground in nutrient-rich soils. Europe, western Asia, northern Africa, North America.*

> **upper flowers in whorls**
> **stem square, hairy**
> **strong, unpleasant smell**

The plant's unpleasant smell and taste are probably to blame for its lack of popularity in folk medicine. Nevertheless, the herb has been used as a remedy for spasmodic coughs, cramps, nausea and hysteria, and, externally, in the treatment of gout. In homeopathy, distillations of the sub-species *B. n. foetida* are prescribed for insomnia.

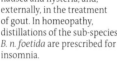

corolla 10–14mm long

calyx toothed

stem angular, hairy

8–20 flowers per whorl

Hollowroot

Corydalis cava (fumitory family)

H 10–35cm   March–May   herbaceous perennial

Habitat *Beech and deciduous forests with rich undergrowth, lowland forests, gardens. Central Europe.*

> **flowers in upright racemes**
> **uppermost petal forms a long spur**
> **2 biternate leaves per stem**

The tuberous root contains a number of alkaloids and is poisonous. In folk medicine it has been used to relieve period pain, to expel intestinal worms and as a sedative. The plant's calmative properties have now been proven and root extracts are used in natural sleep aids and herbal remedies for anxiety.

flowers purple or white

white attachments on seeds

flowers with oval bracts

Burning Bush

Dictamnus albus (rue family)

H 60–120cm   May–June   herbaceous perennial 🕱

This plant is poisonous and prolonged contact with it can lead to phototoxic dermatitis. The 12th century German herbalist Hildegard von Bingen was one of the first to note its medicinal properties, describing it as 'warm and dry' and recommending it for a number of complaints, including heart conditions. In folk medicine, the leaves are used as a vulnerary, for irregular periods and to relieve rheumatic pain.

Habitat *Forest margins, rocky slopes and open woodland. On dry, alkaline soils. Central and southern Europe, Asia Minor.*

> **leaves pinnate with 3–5 leaflet pairs**
> **fragrant, with black glandular hairs**

flowers 4–5cm across

stamens curling up at the tip

petals with dark pattern

49

fruit in 5 sections with several seeds each

leaves odd-pinnate

Did you know?

The flower petals of Burning Bush are rich in volatile essential oils. On very hot days these ignite very easily, hence the plant's name. It is thought to be the species referred to in the bible. Self-medication is not advised due to the plant's toxicity.

Purple Foxglove

Digitalis purpurea ssp. *purpurea* (figwort family)

H 40–150 cm   June–Aug   biennial to perennial

Habitat *Clearings, woodland glades, along waysides. On well-drained, acidic soils. Western Europe.*

> one single upright stem, covered in soft down
> basal rosette only in year one, stem and flowers in year two

corolla 3.5–5cm long

inside of flower with dark blotchy pattern

50

The medicinal substance the Purple Foxglove is now probably best known for was discovered only around 200 years ago – the plant had never played a major role in folk medicine. The dried leaves of Purple Foxglove contain Digitalis glycosides, saponins and other active substances. A substance known as digitoxin is now used in conventional medicine to treat heart failure. In the past, whole-plant extracts had to be adjusted to the requirements of individual patients, but now purified glycosides are used. Only homeopathy still uses extracts from the whole plant.

up to 100 individual flowers per stem

white- and pale-flowering varieties occur

flowers in a one-sided raceme

leaves oval, underside hoary

Did you know?

Foxglove has had an interesting career as a medicinal herb. In the early Middle Ages, Irish monks recommended the plant for sores and ulcers, headaches and paralysis. In 1786, the English physician William Withering discovered its heart-stimulating properties.

Fumitory

Fumaria officinalis ssp. *officinalis* (fumitory family)
H 15–30cm   May–Oct   annual

The dried leaves and flowers of the plant contain a number of alkaloids. Herbalists recommend Fumitory for gall bladder complaints, while in folk medicine it is used to relieve constipation, rheumatic pain, bladder complaints and liver disease. Ancient Arab physicians also considered it an effective cure for melancholy.

Habitat Fields, gardens, wasteland sites, disturbed ground. Europe to central Asia.

> **grows on nutrient-rich soil**
> **flowers in upright racemes**
> **sepals toothed**

flowers 5–8mm long, with spur

leaves biternate

rounded spur

leaflets grey-green

petals with dark red tips

51

Liquorice

Glycyrrhiza glabra (pea family)
H 50–100cm   May–Sept   herbaceous perennial

In addition to its use in confectionery, Liquorice root is applied medicinally for its expectorant and demulcent properties, e.g. in cough syrups and gastritis remedies. The root contains glycyrrhizin, a substance that is 50 times sweeter than sucrose, and has long been used as a flavouring in other medicines to mask their unpleasant taste. It should be used in moderation, however, as prolonged use can raise blood pressure and affect hormonal balance.

Habitat Eastern Mediterranean, south-eastern Asia.

> **root yellow inside, sweet-tasting**
> **leaves pinnate**
> **leaflets long, oval, underside feels sticky**

leaflets long, oval

racemes 8–15cm tall

fibrous root

flowers in tall, upright racemes

Motherwort

Leonurus cardiaca (mint family)
H 30–100cm   June–Sept   herbaceous perennial

corolla 8–12mm in size

Habitat *Disturbed ground, waysides, in hedgerows and gardens. On nutrient-rich soils. Europe, Asia.*

> labiate flowers in dense clusters
> lower leaves lobed, maple-like
> upper leaves unlobed

The green parts of this plant contain a number of active elements (e.g. bitter agents, betaines, flavonoids) with very different properties. They are used medicinally for their antispasmodic action, to regulate the menstrual cycle, encourage and ease uterine contractions and to help lower blood pressure. In addition, the herb is used in folk as well as conventional medicine to treat palpitations, overactive thyroid and symptoms of the menopause.

upper petal upright, helmet-shaped

upper leaves smaller

flowers in whorls

52

Pennyroyal

Mentha pulegium (mint family)
H 10–50cm   June–Sept   herbaceous perennial

Habitat *In moist ground near water. Europe, south-western Asia and northern Africa.*

> aromatic fragrance
> calyx 2-lipped
> leaves oval, margins entire or coarsely toothed

The essential oils present in this plant contain a toxic substance called pule-gone. In folk medicine, the herb has been used as a remedy for digestive disorders, liver and gall bladder complaints and period pain. In higher doses it was also used to induce abortion – often with fatal consequences. In Britain, this plant has declined sharply over the past 50 years and is now listed as a protected plant species.

flowers in dense whorls

labiate flower 5–7mm long

leaf margins entire or coarsely toothed

Peppermint

Mentha piperita (mint family)
H 30–90cm   June–Aug   herbaceous perennial

It seems that the characteristic flavour of Peppermint was popular even with the ancient Egyptians – the plant has been found in graves dating back to 1200 BC. Menthol, the main component within its essential oil, is thought to be responsible for the soothing and antispasmodic effect of Peppermint tea on the gastro-intestinal tract. Whether as a herbal remedy, essential oil or rub, as a herbal tea or as a flavouring and culinary herb, the versatile Peppermint is as popular in conventional and folk medicine as it is in the kitchen.

Habitat *In cultivation and as a garden plant only; occasionally found naturalised in the wild.*

> *sterile hybrid of unknown origin*
> *spreads via rhizomes*

leaves opposite, elliptical, with red leaf veins

flowers in dense spikes

53

stem reddish–purple, glabrous

Health tip

Peppermint tea to settle the stomach: add boiling water to 1 tbsp of fresh or dried Peppermint leaves. Infuse for 5–10 minutes, then strain. Drink several freshly brewed cups throughout the day to ease nausea and intestinal upset.

Bergamot
Monarda didyma (mint family)
H 50–90cm   July–Sept   herbaceous perennial

Habitat *Originally from North America, introduced to Europe as an ornamental plant.*

> *in varieties as a garden plant*
> *wild form with crimson flowers*
> *upper leaves and bracts often red-tinged*

This stunning flower is mostly known as a popular garden plant. However, in its native North America it is also used as a medicinal herb to boost the appetite and soothe the stomach. Responsible for this are the essential oils in the plant's leaves and flowers, while its tannins also made it a useful vulnerary. The edible flowers add colour to summer salads.

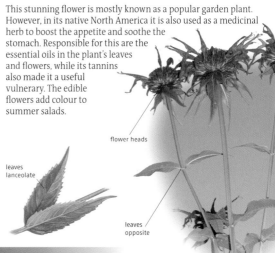

flower heads

terminal flower heads

leaves lanceolate

leaves opposite

Catmint
Nepeta cataria (mint family)
H 40–100cm   July–Sept   herbaceous perennial

Habitat *Wasteland and disturbed ground, along waysides, on walls. Naturalised in central Europe from south-eastern Europe and western Asia.*

> *aromatic fragrance*
> *underside of leaves covered in hoary down*
> *cats are attracted to it*

This plant derives its name from the effect it has on cats: as with Valerian, cats are irresistibly attracted to its scent. However, its active elements are quite different. The leaves contain essential oils and bitter agents with diaphoretic and febrifuge properties. For this, they have been used in folk medicine to treat digestive complaints, colds and fevers. An 18th century Irish herbal recommends Catmint for internal injuries and shortness of breath.

petals pink to yellowish-white

petals 1cm long

leaves stalked, opposite

calyx downy, with 5 teeth

Basil

Ocimum basilicum (mint family)

H 20–50cm   June–Sept   annual

Most people know Basil mainly as a culinary herb. Yet it has a long history throughout the ancient world: in Hinduism it was revered as a holy plant, it was popular with the ancient Egyptians and Greeks – the name Basil is derived from the Greek word basilikós = royal – and the Romans also used it as a culinary and a medicinal herb for digestive complaints and as an antidote to poisoning. More recently, a substance within its essential oil, estragole, has been linked to cancer, and its use as a medicinal plant has declined as a result.

Habitat Native to India, cultivated worldwide as a culinary herb.

> aromatic fragrance
> leaves shiny, leaf margins entire or toothed

flowers red, yellow or white

 55

flowers in loose whorls

leaf veins on older plants red

leaves of young plant used as kitchen herb

different varieties available for culinary use

Health tip

Basil is a key ingredient in the popular and tasty Italian sauce pesto: using a pestle and mortar, pound a large handful of basil leaves with some olive oil. Add pine kernels and garlic. Freshly made pesto is suitable for freezing.

Spiny Restharrow

Ononis spinosa (pea family)
H 30–60cm   June–July   dwarf shrub

Habitat *Nutrient-poor meadows and pastures, along waysides. Often on alkaline soils. Central Europe.*

> *deep taproot*
> *dwarf shrub, woody at base*
> *lower leaves trifoliate, upper leaves simple*

The root of Spiny Restharrow contains flavonoids, essential oils, tannins and a substance called onocerin. The ancient Greek physician Dioscorides already recognised the plant's diuretic properties and both folk and conventional medicine are using it for this purpose. A tea made from Spiny Restharrow is an effective remedy for urinary tract infections and can also prevent bladder stones. In folk medicine it is recommended for rheumatic complaints and gout.

flower with large pink 'shield'

leaves with glandular hairs

56

flower 10–20mm across

long spiny thorns

Health tip

Cleansing herbal tea to flush out the urinary tract: use 2 tsp of chopped restharrow root per cup, add boiling water and infuse for 20–30 minutes, then strain. Drink 2–3 cups per day. Not suitable for people suffering from oedema.

Green-winged Orchid

Orchis morio (orchid family)

H 10–40cm   April–June   herbaceous perennial

The tuberous roots of this plant were known in former times as 'salep'. They are rich in mucilage and a nutritious starch-like substance. The mucilage was used to relieve coughs and throat infections, heartburn and digestive disorders. Children were given orchid root for diarrhoea, and, because of its resemblance to testicles, it was also considered an aphrodisiac.

Habitat Dry, nutrient-poor grassland. Southern to central Europe, northern Africa, western Asia.

> plant is rare in Britain (though not protected by law)
> upper leaves sheath-like
> upper petals with green vertical stripes

lower petal folded lengthwise

root forms 2 egg-shaped tubers

lower petals 3-lobed

Dittany of Crete

Origanum dictamnus (mint family)

H 10–20cm   June–Sept   shrub

This plant occurs naturally on Crete only, where it was regarded as a panacea. Its essential oil contains small amounts of a toxic component called 'pulegone'. Tea from the dried leaves is recommended for stomach and digestive complaints, period pain and uterine disorders. It is also beneficial for oral or throat infections or can be used as a gargle. In modern herbal medicine its use has been superseded by more effective remedies.

Habitat Originally on Crete only, in rock crevices and dry places, in the mountains.

> aromatic fragrance
> a popular culinary herb in Elizabethan Britain
> large, green or pink, scale-shaped flower bracts

flower with distinctive bracts

flower

bracts

leaves soft and velvety

Sweet Marjoram
Origanum majorana (mint family)
H 20–60cm   July–Sept   annual to biennial

Habitat Native to northern Africa and south-western Asia; often cultivated as a culinary herb.

> mainly used as a kitchen herb
> leaves release an aromatic fragrance when bruised

For the ancient Greeks, Marjoram was sacred to Aphrodite, the goddess of love, and was considered an aphrodisiac. They used it as a spice for wine – these days it is mainly known as a culinary herb in sausages and meat dishes. As a medicinal herb it has been used to stimulate the appetite, aid digestion and relieve flatulence. However, while its application as a kitchen spice is unproblematic, its medicinal use has now been questioned. Equally, its long-standing use in cold remedies and chest rubs for children is no longer advised.

individual flower 4mm long

flowers emerge in the axils of scale-like bracts

flowers in a terminal flower head

flowers white to pink

Health tip

Marjoram bath for colds and bronchitis: Add 6 drops of Marjoram essential oil to the bathwater. Breathe in the vapours. Mixing the essential oil with a carrier oil (or dairy cream) first will ensure it blends more evenly throughout your bathwater.

58

Oregano

Origanum vulgare ssp. vulgaris (mint family)
H 20–60cm   July–Sept   herbaceous perennial

Oregano is an important culinary herb, particularly in Greek and Italian cuisines. The herb contains essential oils, tannins and flavonoids and the dried herb has been used in folk medicine for digestive complaints, infections of the respiratory system, as a gargle and to stimulate the appetite.

Habitat Rough grassland, in full sun. Europe, Asia.

> *stem with a reddish tinge*
> *leaves opposite, glandular-dotted*

corolla 4–7mm long

flowers in dense clusters

leaves opposite

59

Summer Savory

Satureja hortensis (mint family)
H 10–25cm   July–Oct   annual

Although Summer Savory is now known mainly as a culinary herb, the Romans thought of it as a nourishing vegetable, as is reflected in the plant's scientific name (from Latin saturare = to saturate). North of the Alps, it was grown in monastic gardens from the 9th century onwards. The herb stimulates the appetite and aids digestion.

Habitat Native to the eastern Mediterranean. Cultivated as a culinary herb throughout Europe.

> *densely branching plant*
> *aromatic fragrance*
> *leaves on short stalks*

labiate flowers, just 5mm in size

leaves linear, opposite

flowers reddish-purple to white

Winter Savory

Satureja montana ssp. *montana* (mint family)

H 10–40cm   July–Oct   herbaceous perennial

Habitat Rocky ground and dry grassland. Southern Europe. Cultivated as a culinary herb.

> dwarf shrub, woody at base
> aromatic fragrance
> leaves sessile

This perennial plant contains the same essential oils as its more short-lived relative, the Summer Savory, and both are used for the same indications. In folk medicine, Savory is used as a remedy for diarrhoea, to relieve flatulence and as a gargle for throat infections.

1–7 flowers per whorl

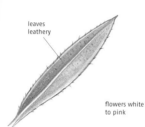

leaves leathery

flowers white to pink

Wood Betony

Stachys officinalis = (*Betonica officinalis*) (mint family)

H 30–100cm   July–Aug   herbaceous perennial

Habitat Heath and moorland, meadows and pastures in mountainous regions. Europe, western Asia, northern Africa.

> labiate flowers in a large spike
> basal leaves on long stalks, upper leaves almost sessile

Betony has been known throughout history as a cure for a multitude of ailments. The chief physician to Emperor Augustus listed it as a certain cure for no less than 47 diseases. Indeed, Pliny the Elder comments on the fact that physicians of his time would always prescribe Betony, whatever the complaint. In folk medicine it has been used as a remedy for diarrhoea, respiratory infections, asthma and as a vulnerary. Modern herbal medicine uses Betony much less, though it is still prescribed in homeopathy.

labiate flower 8–15mm long

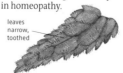

leaves narrow, toothed

leaves opposite

Wall Germander

Teucrium chamaedrys (mint family)

H 15–30cm   July–Aug   dwarf shrub

The dried flowering herb contains essential oils and glycosides. For centuries it was used as a folk remedy for gout, stomach and digestive complaints, to stimulate the appetite and to aid digestion. However, modern medicine advises against its use as it can damage the liver.

Habitat *Rough grassland, slopes, on nutrient-poor, alkaline soils. Central and southern Europe, north-western Africa, south-western Asia.*

> *plant gives off an aromatic fragrance when bruised*
> *spreads through rhizomes*

1–6 flowers in the upper leaf axils

leaf base wedge-shaped

corolla 10–15mm long

Cat Thyme

Teucrium marum (mint family)

H 20–50cm   April–Aug   shrub

This plant is related to Germander, but its essential oils have a slightly different composition. The herb was used in folk medicine to treat bronchitis and as an antispasmodic remedy for stomach, digestive and gall bladder complaints. Today it is mainly used in homeopathy, where it is prescribed for infections of the respiratory system.

Habitat *Islands in the western Mediterranean, evergreen maquis.*

> *strong aromatic fragrance*
> *underside of leaves covered in hoary down*
> *flowers in spikes*

flowers in spikes

unstalked flowers in leaf axils

leaves opposite

stem covered in hoary down

flower 10mm long

Broad-leaved Thyme

Thymus pulegioides ssp. *pulegioides* (mint family)

H 5–40cm   June–Oct   dwarf shrub

Habitat Dry, nutrient-poor meadows and pastures, pine forests. On lime-free soils. Europe.

> woody at base
> stem 4-sided, angular, creeping or decumbent

The herb is collected when in flower. Broad-leaved Thyme contains less essential oil than Common Thyme, but was nevertheless a popular herb in folk medicine. It is known in particular as a cough remedy. As a culinary herb it stimulates the appetite and relieves stomach and digestive disorders, due to the tannins it contains. In mediaeval times, the herb was considered a women's tonic and was taken to relieve period pain and to enhance fertility.

corolla 3–6mm long

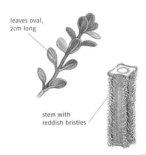

leaves oval, 2cm long

stem with reddish bristles

Health tip

Muscle rub for aching muscles, rheumatic pain and arthritis: add 1/4 litre of rubbing alcohol (surgical spirit with 70% alcohol) to 20g of Broad-leaved Thyme and infuse for 10 days.

flowers in a dense cluster

Common Thyme
Thymus vulgaris (mint family)
H 10–30cm   April–July   dwarf shrub

Thyme in fresh or dried form is a popular culinary herb and is often added to rich food for its digestive action. The essential oils in its leaves contain thymol, which is responsible for its characteristic fragrance. Its medicinal properties were already recognised by the Greek physician Hippocrates, and Common Thyme is listed in 16th century herbals. It is used as a remedy for coughs and digestive disorders, and is a common ingredient in mouthwashes. Nevertheless, it should not be used in large quantities and over extended periods of time.

Habitat *Originally from the western Mediterranean, cultivated in Europe as a culinary and medicinal herb.*

> *dwarf shrub, woody base*
> *leaves sessile, aromatically scented*

flowers in whorls

labiate flower 4–6mm long

 63

underside of leaves downy

flowers white to pale purple

Health tip
Thyme bath to ward off colds and flu: add 1 litre of boiling water to 100g of dried thyme leaves, infuse for 10–15 minutes, then strain through a sieve straight into your bathwater. Stay in the bath for about 10–15 minutes, deeply inhaling the steam. Rest afterwards.

Hare's-foot Clover
Trifolium arvense (pea family)
H 10–30m June–Sept annual

Habitat *Rough grassland, fields, along waysides, in sandy soil. Europe, northern Africa, western Asia.*

> *flowers initially white, then turn pink as they mature*
> *downy sepals*
> *leaves trifoliate, leaflets narrow-oval*

sepals extend beyond petals

Hare's-foot Clover is not used much in medicine. The flowering herb does, however, contain tannins, essential oils and resins and is recommended as a folk remedy for gout and for severe diarrhoea, for which it was used during the post-war years. The herb is collected in summer and is now mainly used in homeopathic preparations.

cylindrical flower heads

leaflets up to 2.5cm long

Red Clover
Trifolium pratense ssp. *pratense* (pea family)
H 15–40cm June–Sept herbaceous perennial

Habitat *Meadows and pastures. On nutrient-rich soils. Europe, Asia.*

> *roots as deep as 2m, form small tubers*
> *flower head spherical or oval*

individual floret 12–18mm long

The dried flower heads were used in folk medicine to treat chronic skin conditions, such as eczema and psoriasis, but also for whooping cough and ulcers. The flowers contain aromatic compounds and plant acids. The white crescent-shaped marks on the leaves were seen in the past as resembling the symptoms of cataract and, according to the Doctrine of Signatures, the plant was therefore thought to be a cure for the disease.

capitulum 1.5–3cm in diameter

leaves with white markings

Garden Nasturtium

Tropaeolum majus (nasturtium family)

Climbing or creeping   June–Oct   annual

Nasturtium originates from the Andes, where the fresh herb was traditionally used as a vulnerary and as an expectorant for coughs and catarrhs. The leaves contain mustard oil glycosides, which break down into a substance with antibiotic properties, called benzyl mustard oil. This has been shown to inhibit the growth of bacteria and fungi. For this, Nasturtium is used in the treatment of respiratory and urinary tract infections. It is contraindicated for gastro-intestinal ulcers, kidney disease and should not be given to small children.

Habitat Native to northern South America, often grown as a garden plant.

> climbs via flower and leaf stalks
> leaves and flowers edible, can be used in salads
> introduced to Europe in 1684

different-coloured flowers on the same plant

flowers yellow-orange to red

65

lower petals fringed at base

leaves peltate (shield-shaped)

Health tip

Nasturtium leaves are rich in vitamin C (about 300mg per 100g of fresh leaves). Finely chopped, they add a peppery flavour to fresh green salads, while the edible flowers can be scattered over as a garnish.

Garlic Mustard
Alliaria petiolata (mustard family)
H 20–100cm   April–June   annual

Habitat *On disturbed ground, forest margins, in hedgerows, gardens, parks. On nutrient-rich soils. Europe, north-western Africa, south-western Asia.*

> **leaves give off a garlic scent when bruised**
> **lower leaves kidney-shaped**

Garlic Mustard is known both as a kitchen herb and a medicinal plant. Although conventional medicine makes no use of it at all, folk medicine utilises the mildly antibiotic properties of the plant's mustard oil glycosides in poultices for slow-healing wounds and in gargles for oral infections. The fresh leaves are rich in provitamin A and vitamin C and make a tasty addition to green salads.

seeds

long, thin, upright seed pods

flowers in small terminal clusters

petals 5–7mm long

66

upper leaves heart-shaped

leaves stalked

Health tip
The young leaves of Garlic Mustard can be harvested throughout spring and summer into early autumn. Finely chopped they add a subtle garlic flavour to fresh salads, but without the unpleasant side effects of real garlic.

Horseradish

Armoracia rusticana (mustard family)
H 60–120cm   May–July   herbaceous perennial

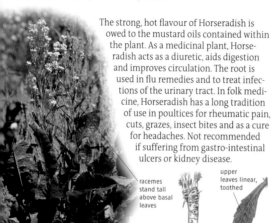

The strong, hot flavour of Horseradish is owed to the mustard oils contained within the plant. As a medicinal plant, Horseradish acts as a diuretic, aids digestion and improves circulation. The root is used in flu remedies and to treat infections of the urinary tract. In folk medicine, Horseradish has a long tradition of use in poultices for rheumatic pain, cuts, grazes, insect bites and as a cure for headaches. Not recommended if suffering from gastro-intestinal ulcers or kidney disease.

Habitat Wasteland sites, on disturbed ground, in ditches and gardens. Naturalised on nutrient-rich soils.

> seed pods almost spherical
> basal leaves up to 1m long
> multitude of small white flowers in long, branching racemes

racemes stand tall above basal leaves

fleshy root

upper leaves linear, toothed

flowers 5–9mm in diameter

67

Shepherd's Purse

Capsella bursa-pastoris (mustard family)
H 10–70cm   Jan–Dec   annual to biennial

The fruits are the key identifying feature on this otherwise inconspicuous plant. The green parts contain flavonoids, plant acids, salts and a peptide with haemostatic action. This medicinal property was recognised very early on and Shepherd's Purse has been employed throughout history in the treatment of cuts and grazes, nose bleeds and uterine haemorrhages. Folk medicine uses the herb in depurative teas.

Habitat Wasteland sites, on disturbed ground, edges of fields, in gardens. On nutrient-rich soils. In most parts of the world.

> indicates nitrogen-rich soils
> colonising plant
> up to 40,000 seeds per individual plant

pods triangular or heart-shaped

stem with fruit capsules on long stalks

upper leaves clasping the stem

petals just 3mm long

seed pods 4–10mm long

Cuckoo Flower
Cardamine pratensis (mustard family)
H 10–60cm   April–June   herbaceous perennial

white, pink or
pale violet flowers

Habitat *Damp meadows and pastures, fens and marshes, lowland forests, near water. Northern hemisphere.*

> *preferred host plant for caterpillar of the orange-tip butterfly*
> *flowers white, pink or violet*

The plant's name relates to its flowering time, which coincides with the cuckoo's arrival. Other names are Lady's Smock, Meadow Cress and Cuckoo Spit. The latter refers to the characteristic frothy secretions of the froghopper larva, to which the plant is host. The plant is used in homeopathy to supplement diabetes therapy. In folk medicine, the leaves were added to fresh salads for their high vitamin C content and depurative properties.

petals up to 2cm long

seed pods thin (1mm), stalk-like

new plants grow in axils of basal leaves

Scurvy Grass
Cochlearia officinalis (mustard family)
H 20–50cm   May–June   biennial to perennial

upper leaves sessile

Habitat *Sea cliffs, salt and coastal marshes. In western, northern and central Europe, including Britain.*

> *leaves wintergreen*
> *stem angular, ribbed*
> *basal leaves fleshy*

flowers lightly fragrant

flowers in dense clusters

As the name suggests, the plant is rich in vitamin C and was eaten by sailors to keep the dreaded scurvy at bay. In folk medicine, the herb was used as a diuretic, to aid digestion and stimulate the appetite, and as a remedy for stomach complaints, rheumatism and gout. Poultices of the leaves were placed on ulcers.

petals 3–7mm long

basal leaves kidney-shaped

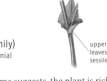

European Spindle

Euonymus europaeus var. *europaeus* (spindle family)

H 1.50–3m   May–June   shrub   ☠

The distinctive fruits contain cardiac glycosides, alkaloids, bitter agents, tannins and lectins. They are highly poisonous and are no longer recommended for medicinal use, except in homeopathic preparations. In former times they were used to treat heart conditions. Their most important application, however, was as a treatment for skin parasites such as lice and scabies.

Habitat *Forest margins, hedgerows, lowland forests, along the banks of streams. On nutrient-rich soils. Europe, Asia Minor.*

> *green branches angular, with narrow cork wings*
> *leaves opposite*

fruit in 4 sections, splits open to release orange seeds

seeds

petals narrow, up to 5mm long

ripe fruit capsule conspicuous, bright pink and orange

leaves oval, finely toothed

69

Manna Ash

Fraxinus ornus (olive family)

H 6–15m   April–May   tree

leaves odd-pinnate

The manna produced by this tree has nothing but its name in common with the Biblical manna. Nevertheless, this dried exudate from the bark was a popular delicacy in mediaeval times – imports of manna from Sicily are recorded in Venice as early as the 9th century. Its main ingredient is mannitol, a sugar alcohol, which is used as a gentle laxative and a sugar substitute for diabetics.

Habitat *Mixed deciduous forests in southern Europe and Asia Minor.*

> *cultivated in Sicily*
> *deciduous*
> *fruit pendant, tongue-shaped*

'manna' from dried bark exudate

scented flowers

petals linear, 5–6mm long

Sweet Woodruff

Galium odoratum (bedstraw family)
H 15–30cm   May–June   herbaceous perennial

Habitat Herbaceous undergrowth of mixed and deciduous forests, especially beech forests. On compost-rich soils. Europe, Asia.

> **distinctive coumarin fragrance once dried**
> **traditionally used as a strewing herb**

flower funnel-shaped with 4 lobes

An 18th century Irish herbal recommends Sweet Woodruff as a vulnerary and a treatment for boils and ulcers. The herb is collected just before it comes into flower and, once dried, gives off a characteristic coumarin scent. In conventional medicine it is used to produce an anticoagulant drug for the treatment of varicose veins and other venous diseases. Folk medicine employs it for a much wider range of conditions, from insomnia, anxiety and nervous tension to haemorrhoids and heart conditions. Do not use when pregnant or if taking other cardiovascular medication.

fruit in 2 spherical sections

leaves in whorls

flower 4–6mm across

Health tip

Woodruff tea as a natural sleep aid: use 1 tsp of the herb per cup, add boiling water, infuse for 5 mins and strain. Sweeten to taste with honey and drink immediately. If taken in excess, Woodruff can cause headaches and dizziness.

Goosegrass

Galium aparine (bedstraw family)
H 60–200cm   June–Oct   annual

Seeds of this plant have been found in large quantities in Neolithic settlements. It is thought that the herb was used to curdle milk for cheesemaking. In folk medicine, Goosegrass was recommended for skin conditions, wounds and ulcers (external as well as internal ones), and as a diuretic for bladder complaints.

Habitat *Open and disturbed ground, wasteland sites, forest margins, in hedgerows. On nutrient-rich soils. Almost worldwide.*

> *entire plant covered in sticky hooks (also known as 'Sticky Weed', 'Grip Grass' or 'Cleavers')*
> *stems weak, creeping or climbing*
> *prefers loamy soil*

'sticky' leaves and stalks

leaves in whorls

flowers just 2mm across

71

Wild Candytuft

Iberis amara (mustard family)
H 10–40cm   May–Aug   annual to biennial

The flowering herb is said to stimulate the digestive glands and increase bile flow. It has antibiotic properties but also contains bitter cucurbitacin, a mild poison. Preparations from its seeds are used in homeopathy to treat palpitations and other heart conditions. The plant has been known since antiquity.

Habitat *Edges of fields, chalk grassland, quarries. Southern and western Europe. In northern Europe and Britain rarely in the wild, but grown as a garden plant*

> *plant softly hairy*
> *leaves linear to wedge-shaped, toothed*

young flowers in umbrella-shaped umbels

flowers in umbels

petals unevenly sized

Holly
Ilex aquifolium (holly family)
H 1–6m   May–June   shrub   ☠

Habitat Forests. In sandy or stony ground. Western and central Europe, including Britain, from Norway to Germany south to the Mediterranean and north-western Africa.

> native, evergreen woodland plant
> male and female flowers on separate plants

male flowers in the leaf axils

The leaves of the Holly tree, not its poisonous berries, are the parts of most medicinal interest. They are used in homeopathic remedies for flu, conjunctivitis and other eye infections; folk medicine recommends them for fevers, rheumatic complaints and bronchitis; and in Bach flower remedies, Holly helps to overcome irritability, anger, envy and suspicion.

leaves evergreen, with sharp, spiny margins

leaves dark green, shiny, leathery

bright red berries

72

Watercress
Nasturtium officinale (mustard family)
H 20–80cm   May–Oct   herbaceous perennial

Habitat Along streams and ditches, near springs. Only in fresh, clean water. Worldwide.

> some varieties grow completely submerged
> partly wintergreen
> popular winter vegetable in mediaeval times

anthers yellow

Watercress leaves are rich in mustard oils, vitamin C and minerals. They are popular in fresh salads and are often recommended as part of a detox diet. In former times, Watercress was eaten to prevent scurvy. It aids digestion, acts as a diuretic and has antibiotic properties. The herb is listed in all major historic herbals.

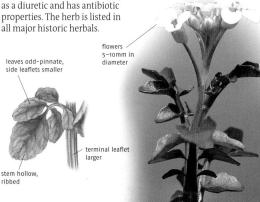

flowers 5–10mm in diameter

leaves odd-pinnate, side leaflets smaller

terminal leaflet larger

stem hollow, ribbed

Olive Tree

Olea europaea ssp. *europaea* (olive family)

H 6–15m   May–June   tree

The Olive Tree has been known since Biblical times. In Mediterranean folk medicine, the leaves are sometimes used in herbal
teas. However, mostly the oil is used: as a lubricant, to relieve constipation or, mixed with garlic, to treat joint and muscle aches.
In conventional medicine it is used as a carrier oil for fat-soluble
medications and in the treatment of skin conditions. Yet, above
all, olive oil is a valuable and cholesterol-lowering cooking oil. In
Bach flower remedies, Olive is recommended for exhaustion and
mental fatigue.

Habitat Evergreen
maquis, primarily
in cultivation.
Mediterranean region.

> *cultivated since antiquity*
> *evergreen*
> *one of the healthiest oils
> for use in cooking and
> salads*

underside
of leaves
slivery-
white

leaves
evergreen

olives first
green, then
deep brown
to black

flower with 4 lobes

73

flower 4–7mm across

leaves hard,
leathery

Health tip

*Olive oil vinaigrette:
mix two finely chop-
ped shallots with some
mustard and garlic to
taste. Add vinegar and
season with salt and
black pepper. Leave for
a few minutes to allow
the flavours to mingle,
then add 50ml of good
quality cold-pressed,
extra-virgin olive oil.*

Radish
Raphanus sativus (mustard family)
H 30–80cm   May–Oct   annual to biennial

Habitat *Cultivated worldwide in many varieties.*

> plant covered in coarse hairs
> root varies in colour and shape depending on cultivar
> seed pods up to 9cm long

The fresh root of this plant is rich in vitamin C and contains mustard oil glycosides, which are responsible for its sharp taste. The juice from the root stimulates the digestive glands, increases bile flow and is thought to help prevent gallstones – although it is not recommended if already suffering from gallstones or gastritis. In folk medicine, the sweetened juice is a popular cough remedy. A black-skinned variety is used in homeopathy for the treatment of stomach and digestive complaints and oily skin.

petals with dark veins

leaves deeply lobed

petals white or violet

74

Health tip

Radish cough syrup: grate one large Radish and mix with 3–4 tbsp of honey. Cover and leave to infuse for about 10 hours, then strain the juice through a sieve. Take one spoonful of the juice at intervals.

Ground Elder

Aegopodium podagraria (parsley family)

H 50–90cm   June–July   herbaceous perennial

The plant is notorious as a stubborn garden weed. However, for centuries it was also held in high repute as a medicinal plant. Indeed, it is thought to have been introduced to Britain by mediaeval monks, who cultivated it in their herb gardens. Tea from the leaves has a diuretic action and was taken for rheumatic pain, diarrhoea and infections, and applied externally to treat haemorrhoids. Poultices of the fresh leaves were placed on burns, stings, wounds and painful joints. The plant is also used in homeopathy to treat gout and arthritis, indeed, one of its older names is Goutweed.

Habitat Damp forests, gardens, parks, near water. On nutrient-rich soils. Europe, western Asia.

> very invasive plant that spreads via rhizomes
> hollow, ribbed stem
> young leaves can be eaten in salads or cooked like spinach

compound umbel with 15–25 smaller umbels

individual flower just 3mm in size

75

stolons

creeping rhizomes

leaves biternate, similar to Elder leaves

Health tip

Ground Elder tea for sciatica and rheumatic pain: use 2 tsp of fresh, young Ground Elder leaves per cup, add boiling water and infuse for 10 minutes, then strain. Drink one cup per day.

Bishop's Weed

Ammi majus (parsley family)

H 30–100cm   June–Sept   annual

Habitat Wasteland sites, fallow ground, along waysides. Mediterranean region, south-western Asia, in central Europe as garden escapes only.

> umbels with up to 60 rays
> stem glabrous

The plant has no history in central European folk medicine, but the seeds are now used medicinally. They contain furanocoumarins, from which a drug is derived for the treatment of psoriasis and vitiligo (patchy depigmentation of the skin). The ingredient responsible for this is called 'methoxypsoralen'. It stimulates the production of pigmentation in skin exposed to ultra-violet light.

feathery bracts

umbel rays spread out

upper leaves bi- to tri-pinnate

Khella

Ammi visnaga (parsley family)

H 20–100cm   April–Aug   annual

Habitat Disturbed ground on damp soil, meadows. South-western Asia, southern Mediterranean.

> umbel rays are used as toothpicks (also known as 'Toothpick Plant')
> all leaves tri-pinnate, leaflets thin and feathery

It is thought that the plant's antispasmodic properties were already known to the ancient Egyptians. It contains a chemical compound known as 'khellin', which has a relaxing effect on internal organs, e.g. bronchi, stomach, digestive tract, gall bladder and urinary system. Another substance, 'visnadine', widens the coronary arteries without affecting the peripheral blood vessels.

umbel with 30–150 rays

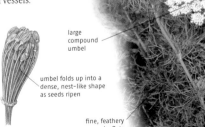

large compound umbel

umbel folds up into a dense, nest-like shape as seeds ripen

fine, feathery leaflets

Chervil

Anthriscus cerefolium ssp. *cerefolium* (parsley family)

H 30–70cm   May–Aug   annual

umbel of flowers

umbel of seeds

The fresh herb contains flavonoids and essential oils (estragole). The leaves are often used as a flavouring and are an essential ingredient in a 'bouquet garni'. The herb aids digestion and acts as a diuretic. In the past, the juice was also used to treat eczema and slow-healing wounds. The ancient Egyptians must have thought highly of the herb, as it was found in the tomb of Pharaoh Tutankhamen.

Habitat Native to south-eastern Europe and Asia. Cultivated in central and western Europe since the 16th century.

> *leaves used as a culinary herb*
> *plant covered in soft hairs, gives off a faint aniseed fragrance*

small umbels on short stalks

seeds upright, with a slender, ridged beak

leaves bi- or tri-pinnate

Celery

Apium graveolens (parsley family)

H 30–100cm   April–Oct   biennial

Both stalks and root are eaten, both raw and cooked. Most potent for medicinal use, however, are the seeds, which contain a complex essential oil. Taken as tea they act as a diuretic, aid digestion and stimulate the appetite. The plant's often cited aphrodisiac effect, however, is unproven. A sweetened decoction from the root was used as a cough syrup. Contraindicated for kidney infections.

Habitat Coastal marshes and in cultivation.

> *prefers saline soils*
> *available as a vegetable in a variety of cultivars*
> *strong fragrance*

Celery root known as Celeriac

fruit in sections with 3 pale-brown ridges

umbel on short stalks or sessile

Bearberry
Arctostaphylos uva-ursi (heather family)
H 20–60cm   March–July   shrub   ✻

Habitat *Open pine forests, heaths and moors. On dry soils. Europe, Asia, North America.*

> evergreen
> dwarf shrub with creeping stems, up to 150cm long

Records show that this plant was used as a medicinal herb by the Welsh 'Physicians of Myddfai' in the 13th century. Both modern and folk medicine recommend a tea from its leaves for infections of the urinary tract. Although the plant has been well-researched, its active substances are not yet completely understood. However, it is rich in tannins, which may explain its application as a remedy for diarrhoea. Bearberry should not be used during pregnancy as it can impair the supply of blood to the foetus.

bell-shaped flower with 5 flared tips

78

leaves shiny, leathery

flared tips reddish-pink

flowers in pendent clusters

berries with remnant of style

Black Chokeberry

Aronia melanocarpa var. *melanocarpa* (rose family)
H 20–300cm   May–June   shrub

The Chokeberry's career as a medicinal plant began relatively recently. Its fruits are one of the richest sources of phenolic substances, mainly tannins, as well as vitamins K and C. The phenols are important antioxidants and include compounds that may help prevent cancer and cardiac disease. In Russia, the berries are known as a remedy for high blood pressure and skin diseases.

Habitat Wetland areas in North America. Cultivated in eastern Europe, garden plant.

> deciduous
> leaves ovate, finely toothed

flowers 1cm across

ripe berries black

79

Sweet Pepper

Capsicum annuum (nightshade family)
H 20–50cm   June–Sept   annual to biennial

plant bears flowers and fruits at the same time

Peppers and chillis are rich in vitamin C and some varieties contain large amounts of volatile essential oils and are extremely hot (e.g. chillis). Their juice has been used in plasters, tinctures and poultices to improve circulation and ease rheumatic pain and muscle stiffness. Chillis and peppers used as spices (cayenne pepper, paprika), which stimulate saliva flow and aid digestion.

Habitat Native to central America but cultivated worldwide. Mediterranean region, eastern and western Europe.

> wide range of cultivars
> leaves on long stalks
> Chilli juice can irritate the skin and eyes

petals fused

red pepper

chilli fruit

Red Bryony

Bryonia cretica ssp. dioica (gourd family)

H 2–4m   June–Sept   herbaceous perennial

Habitat Waste ground, in hedgerows and gardens. On nutrient-rich soils. Southern and central Europe, including Britain, northern Africa.

> climbs via tendrils
> male and female flowers on separate plants
> male flowers in racemes, female flowers in umbels of 2–5
> also known as 'English Mandrake' or 'False Mandrake'

male flowers with green veins

80

root often shaped like a human body (similar to Mandrake)

Did you know?

In mediaeval medicine, the magical powers of a plant were seen as of equal importance as their pharmaceutical properties. The root of Red Bryony resembles the shape of a human body. It was therefore considered an all-heal with magical powers, similar to the Mandrake.

Red Bryony is extremely poisonous. Its active substances affect the lining of the gut and – despite the risks – the plant was used in mediaeval times as a strong purgative. The root was also applied externally to treat gout and rheumatic pain. In homeopathic dilution the plant is safe to use and is prescribed for pleurisy and peritonitis, respiratory infections and liver complaints.

berries 5–8mm in size

female flower

Caraway

Carum carvi (parsley family)

H 30–80cm   May–July   biennial

fruit in 2 halves, 3.5mm long

The essential oils in this plant give Caraway seeds their characteristic flavour. They are traditionally used to flavour breads and cakes and are often added to cabbage dishes. The essential oils are also responsible for the plant's antispasmodic, digestive and carminative properties. A tea made from Caraway seeds relieves gastro-intestinal complaints and flatulent colic, and in folk medicine it is used to increase milk flow in nursing mothers.

Habitat Meadows and pastures, along waysides. On nutrient-rich soils. Europe to Asia, northern Africa.

> *fruits release an aromatic fragrance when crushed*
> *stem angular, leaves pinnate*
> *small umbels on stalks of varying length*

flowers white, sometimes with a reddish tinge

lower leaves opposite

compound umbel with 8–16 smaller umbels

Pipsissewa

Chimaphila umbellata (wintergreen family)

H 10–20cm   June–Aug   herbaceous perennial

The green parts of this plant contain tannins, flavonoids and arbutin, a substance that has proven helpful in the treatment of urinary tract infections. Whereas in Europe it is primarily used in homeopathy, North American Indians have traditionally known this plant as a remedy for kidney and bladder infections, period pain, rheumatic complaints and skin diseases.

flowers white to pink

Habitat Open pine forests. Northern, central and eastern Europe to Asia, North America.

> *creeping rhizomes*
> *leaves evergreen*
> *flowers nodding*

petals 5–6mm long

leaves rosette-like

Lemon

Citrus limon (rue family)
H 5–10m   March–Sept   tree

Habitat *Originally from northern India, now cultivated worldwide. Mediterranean region.*

> evergreen tree
> spiny thorns in the leaf axils
> leaves opposite

Lemons contain twice as much vitamin C as oranges and are well known as a preventative medicine to ward off colds. In addition, the rind of not fully ripened lemons has a number of medicinal uses. It contains essential oils, bioflavonoids and plant acids and is used in folk medicine, aromatherapy and conventional medicine. The dried peel is often added as a flavouring to mixed herbal and fruit teas. Other applications make use of the plant's antiseptic properties.

lemon peel contains essential oils

leaves oval to lanceolate, leathery

petals pink on the outside

82

Health tip

To soothe a sore throat, try a 1:1 mix of lemon juice and hot water. As a remedy for colds, a drink of lemon juice and hot water (1:2) with some crushed garlic and cinnamon and perhaps some grated ginger root is recommended.

Bitter Orange
Citrus aurantium (rue family)
H 4–5m March–May tree

leaf stalks
winged

All parts of Bitter Orange are used for medicinal purposes: unripened fruits, rind, flowers and leaves, or rather, the essential oils contained in all of these. The flowers, prepared as an aromatic infusion, are said to have calming properties and help relieve coughs. The bitter-tasting rind stimulates the appetite and aids digestion. The oil is used in cosmetics and as a flavouring in food and drinks.

Habitat Originally from south-eastern Asia, cultivated in the Mediterranean.

> small tree with a rounded crown
> evergreen
> spiny thorns in the leaf axils

round fruits, yellow to orange

up to 20 stamens

petals with dark specks on the outside

Field Bindweed
Convolvulus arvensis (bindweed family)
H 20–80cm June–Sept herbaceous perennial

This plant's glory days as a medicinal plant are most probably over, as better laxative and diuretic preparations are now available. Its leaves contain glycosides, tannins and flavonoids, which aggravate the digestive tract too much. The mediaeval German herbalist Hildegard von Bingen described it as 'not very useable'. Nevertheless, the fresh, flowering plant is still utilised in homeopathy to treat back ache.

Habitat Fields, gardens, vineyards, waste ground, waysides. Virtually worldwide.

> colonising plant, prefers loamy soils
> roots as deep as 2m
> pernicious weed

each flower opens for one day only

leaves spear-shaped

flowers on long stalks

trumpet-shaped flower, up to 2.5cm long

flower bud

Coriander
Coriandrum sativum (parsley family)
H 20–60cm   June–July   annual

Habitat *Wasteland, disturbed ground, fields. On nutrient-rich soils. Originally from the eastern Mediterranean, cultivated throughout most of the world.*

> *fresh plant has an strong smell, which some find unpleasant*
> *leaves pinnate, upper leaves thin and feathery, lower leaves rounded*

umbel with 3–5 rays

Fresh Coriander leaves are a regular ingredient in Thai food, and the dried fruits ('coriander seeds') are used in curries and as a flavouring in cakes and bread. They contain essential oils (up to 75% linalool) and other substances to varying degrees. Coriander stimulates the digestive glands and thereby aids digestion, it relieves bloating and flatulence and has antispasmodic properties. The dried herb is often added as a flavouring in herbal teas.

leaflets on upper leaves narrow and feathery

fruits ('seeds') round, ribbed

flowers white to pale pink

84

Health tip
Herbal infusion to relieve wind and bloating: mix Aniseed, Fennel, Coriander and Cumin seeds (1:1:1:2) and crush using a pestle and mortar. Use 2 tsp of the mix per cup, add hot water and strain after 10 minutes. Drink unsweetened.

Midland Hawthorn

Crataegus laevigata (rose family)

H 4–10m   May–June   small tree or shrub

The Midland Hawthorn is less widespread in Britain than the Common Hawthorn (*Crataegus monogyna*). Its key distinguishing feature is that the flower of the Midland Hawthorn has two styles, whereas that of Common Hawthorn has just one. Medicinally, however, the two plants are used interchangeably. The flowers and young shoots contain flavonoids and a number of plant acids. Hawthorn is used in the same way as Digitalis and preparations are prescribed for a wide range of heart conditions. In folk medicine, puréed Hawthorn berries are a remedy for diarrhoea.

Habitat *Forest margins, shrubland, hedgerows, heaths, in parks. Most of Europe, though less common in Britain.*

> **spiny thorns**
> **leaves alternate, less deeply lobed than those of Common Hawthorn**

leaves oval, shallowly lobed

anthers conspicuous

flower with two styles

flowers in loose umbels

bright red, round to oval berries

Health tip

Hawthorn tea to strengthen the heart and improve circulation: use 1 tsp of hawthorn flowers per cup. Add hot water and infuse for 20 minutes, then strain. Drink 3–4 cups throughout the day.

Cumin

Cuminum cyminum (parsley family)
H 20–30cm   June–July   annual

seeds
oblong,
ridged

Habitat Native to
northern Africa (Egypt)
and south-western
Asia, cultivated in
Spain, France and
Sicily.

> medicinal plant of the
  Egyptian pharaohs
> used as a spice, similar
  to Caraway
> leaves feathery

Cumin has a long history as a medicinal and culinary herb.
The ancient Egyptians knew about its healing properties and
recommended it for digestive disorders, coughs and toothache. It
was used to the same effect in mediaeval times. In addition, the
fruits were used to stimulate menstrual flow and – in larger doses
– to induce abortion.

flowers white
to pink

leaves
narrow,
feathery

86

Quince

Cydonia oblonga (rose family)
H 4–8m   May–June   small tree or shrub

Habitat Native to
south-western Asia,
cultivated worldwide
as a fruit tree.

> shrub or small tree
> fruits only edible once
  cooked

solitary flowers,
white to pale
pink

Raw quinces are unpalatable, but cooked
they are an ideal ingredient in jams, jellies
and sweets. In folk medicine, Quince juice
is used as a gargle and mouthwash to treat
mouth ulcers, gum problems and sore
throats. The seeds swell when soaked in
water and the resulting mucilage can be
used as a cough remedy or applied
externally to minor burns
and dry, chapped skin.

petals up to 3cm long

fruits look similar to apples or
pears, depending on variety

Thorn Apple

Datura stramonium (nightshade family)

H 30–120cm   June–Oct   annual ☠

Cases of *Datura* poisoning are relatively rare – perhaps the fruit's spiky appearance acts as a deterrent in itself. However, the plant contains tropane alkaloids and there have been reports of people attempting to use it as a recreational drug. Unfortunately, over-dosing is extremely easy and can be fatal or cause brain damage. The species was introduced to Europe in the 16th century, but naturalised quickly. The dried leaves were used in the past as a remedy for asthma, spasmodic coughs and Parkinson's disease. In homeopathy, the plant is still in use as a treatment for infections and fever, eye infections and mental illness.

Habitat Rubble and waste ground, along waysides. Introduced to Europe from Central America as an orna-mental and medicinal plant, occasionally found in the wild.

> leaves up to 20cm long
> calyx ridged, tube-shaped
> food plant for moths

corolla with sharply pointed flared tips

flowers trumpet-shaped

corolla up to 10cm long

calyx tubular

87

spiky fruit capsule

seeds black, kidney-shaped

Did you know?

Native American shamans used Datura in rituals and cere-monies. However, they were also aware of the danger of overdose, as is expressed in their saying 'Eat a little and go to sleep. Eat some more and have a dream. Eat some more and never wake up'.

Wild Carrot
Daucus carota (parsley family)
H 30–100cm   June–Sept   biennial

Strictly speaking, the Wild Carrot is not a medicinal plant as such. However, it is a very healthy vegetable and a rich source of vitamins, in particular provitamin A and vitamins B and C. In former times, fresh carrot juice was used to expel intestinal worms, and soft-cooked carrots were given to children as a remedy for diarrhoea. Herbals tend to recommend the wild form of the plant over cultivated varieties. The seeds have a diuretic action and were also taken to induce abortion.

seeds in a nest-shaped umbel

umbel with black flower in its centre

feathery bracts

88

individual flowers 3mm in size

vegetable carrot

Health tip
Freshly pressed carrot or vegetable juice is a depurative and supplies the body with important vitamins. Good combinations are: carrots and broccoli; carrots, tomatoes and cucumber; or carrots and fresh fruit. Add a little cream or oil to help the body absorb the provitamin A.

Round-leaved Sundew

Drosera rotundifolia (sundew family)
H 5–20cm   July–Aug   herbaceous perennial

Sundew grows mainly in Sphagnum bogs, which are rare and usually protected habitats. Its leaves contain flavonoids, plant acids and an aromatic compound called naphthoquinone. This is used in conventional as well as folk medicine and in homeopathy to relieve heavy, spasmodic coughs. In folk medicine, the plant is also used externally to treat corns, warts and bunions, and to reduce the appearance of freckles.

Habitat In peaty soil, raised bogs and moors, near springs. Northern Europe, Asia, North America.

> **carnivorous plant**
> **all leaves basal**

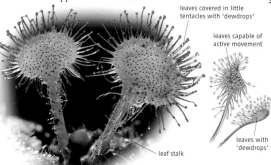

leaves covered in little tentacles with 'dewdrops'

leaves capable of active movement

petals 5mm long

leaf stalk

leaves with 'dewdrops'

sepals

 89

Field Eryngo

Eryngium campestre (parsley family)
H 15–60cm   July–Sept   herbaceous perennial

The leaves and roots of this plant contain saponins, flavonoids and plant acids. Its effectiveness as a medicinal plant is unproven and its only applications are in folk medicine. The root is thought to help with kidney and bladder complaints, prevent the build-up of stones, and is used as a remedy for coughs and bronchitis, while the leaves are recommended for infections of the urinary tract.

Habitat Edges of fields, waysides, rough grass-land and railway embankments. Mainly Mediterranean region, but also central Europe and south-western Asia.

> **individual flowers small and inconspicuous**
> **leaves spiny and stiff, thistle-like**
> **narrow, spiny bracts surrounding the flower head**

long spiny bracts

spiny leaves

flowers in a globular umbel, 15mm in size

Common Buckwheat

Fagopyrum esculentum (knotweed family)

H 20–60cm   July–Oct   annual

Habitat Native to central Asia, in Europe in cultivation, occasionally naturalised on waysides.

> plant can be toxic to grazing animals
> reddish stalks
> calyx white to pink
> cultivated as a starchy cereal

Archaeological evidence suggests that Buckwheat was grown as a crop by the Scythians in the early Iron Age, though its use is thought to date back even further. By the Middle Ages it was widely used throughout Europe. The fruits do not yield a flour suitable for bread-making, but buckwheat was often added as a 'filler'. Usually it was eaten as a porridge or in pancakes (blinis). The leaves contain fagopyrin and rutin, a glycoside which strengthens capillary walls, and are used in folk medicine as a venous tonic and to reduce the risk of arteriosclerosis.

leaves heart- or arrow- shaped

calyx 2–3mm long

90

flowers in dense clusters

Health tip

Buckwheat tea to help prevent arteriosclerosis: use 1 tsp of the chopped herb per cup. Place into a saucepan with water and boil for 1 minute. Leave to settle for 10 minutes and strain. Drink 2–3 cups per day for about a month.

Meadowsweet
Filipendula ulmaria (rose family)
H 50–150cm   June–Aug   herbaceous perennial

Meadowsweet was a sacred herb of the Druids and has a long history as a medicinal plant. The sweetly scented flowers contain essential oils, flavonoids and tannins. They also contain salicylic acid, from which aspirin is derived. Tea made from the dried flowers has a diaphoretic action, which is utilised in the treatment of colds and fevers. In folk medicine, it is also known as a kidney and bladder tonic, a remedy for rheumatic complaints and gout and as a vulnerary. However, excessive use can irritate the stomach. Not suitable for people with aspirin sensitivity.

leaves pinnate, leaflets unevenly sized

Habitat Ditches, streams, riverbanks, near springs, lowland forests, wetland meadows. Europe, Asia.

> *outer flower stalks longer than those in the centre*
> *flowers strongly fragrant*
> *active substances have been used to synthesise aspirin*

petals up to 5mm long

outer flower stalks taller than those in centre

fruits tightly curled up

Health tip
Meadowsweet tea to induce sweating: use 1–2 tsp of dried Meadowsweet flowers per cup. Add boiling water and leave to infuse for 10 minutes. Strain and drink immediately.

Wild Strawberry

Fragaria vesca var. *vesca* (rose family)
H 5–20cm   May–June   herbaceous perennial

Habitat *Open wood-land, forest margins. On nutrient-rich soils. Europe, Asia.*

> **flower stalks with fine, clasping hairs**
> **spreads via stolons**

However delicious the fruits may be, the leaves are the part of this plant with the healing properties. They are rich in tannins and also contain essential oils and flavonoids. In conventional medicine they are not used, but they are an ingredient in many herbal tea mixes (occasionally dried fruits are also added). In folk medicine, the leaves and roots were recommended for diarrhoea, throat infections, rheumatic complaints, gout and liver disease.

flower 10–15mm across

92

fruits deflexed

leaves trifoliate, serrate

ripe fruit detaches from calyx

Health tip

Wild Strawberry tea: add boiling water to 1–2 tsp of dried leaves and infuse for 15 minutes. Strain and drink immediately or use as a gargle for sore throats.

Alder Buckthorn

Frangula alnus = (*Rhamnus frangula*) (buckthorn family)
H 1–4m   May–June   tree or shrub   ☠

Alder Buckthorn is highly poisonous and should not be used for self-medication. In mediaeval times, the bark was used as a purgative – with dangerous side effects, as its active substances prevent fluid absorption from the colon. It has also been used as a slimming aid and to induce abortion.

Habitat *Bogs, lowland forests, shrubland and open woodland. On damp and wet ground. Europe, northern Africa, Asia.*

> **deciduous, leaves alternate**
> **branches without thorns**
> **flowers and fruits are present simultaneously**

berries 8mm in diameter

fruits first red, then black

leaves round to oval

flowers tiny, in small umbels

Water Avens

Geum rivale (rose family)
H 30–70cm   April–July   herbaceous perennial

thick root

The root contains tannins and essential oils. When dried it releases a substance called eugenol, which is also present in cloves. Folk medicine uses the root as a remedy for diarrhoea, digestive complaints and loss of appetite, and as a gargle or mouthwash for coughs and oral or throat infections. The Wood Avens (*Geum urbanum*) has an even higher eugenol content.

Habitat *Bogs, wet meadows, in ditches and along streams, lowland forests. Central Europe, Asia, North America.*

> **petals white to pink**
> **stem upright, downy**
> **indicates nutrient-rich soil**

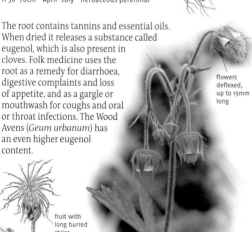

flowers deflexed, up to 15mm long

sepals maroon-coloured

fruit with long burred styles

detail of burs

Black Hellebore
Helleborus niger ssp. *niger* (buttercup family)
H 10–30cm   Dec–April   herbaceous perennial

Habitat Beech and
pine forests. On
compost- and nutrient-
rich, alkaline soils.
Southern and eastern
Alps, Apennines.

> common garden plant
> leaves wintergreen
> solitary flowers on fleshy,
  unbranched stalks

This plant is highly poisonous and its root is now only used
in homeopathy, where it is prescribed for diarrhoea, kidney
infections and depression. Its medicinal properties have been
known since antiquity. The herbalist Nicholas Culpepper
recommends it 'against all melancholy diseases', such as 'quartan
agues and madness'. In folk medicine, the root was used as a
remedy for constipation and to expel intestinal worms. The plant
contains cardiac glycosides and has been used as a heart stimulant.

flower up to 10cm
in diameter

root

leaves fleshy,
palmate or
digitate

petals
spread-out

flower stalk
unbranched

94

Did you know?
According to Pliny,
Hellebore was used as a
cure for mania. In Greek
mythology, the daugh-
ters of King Proitos of
Argos were driven mad
by the god Dionysos as
punishment for scorn-
ing his worship. The
seer Melampos found
them in the mountains
and cured them with
hellebore root.

Black Henbane
Hyoscyamus niger (nightshade family)
H 20–80cm   June–Oct   annual to biennial   ☠

Together with Deadly Nightshade, the highly poisonous Black
Henbane was one of the herbs used by witches to make their
'flying ointments', which gave them the illusion of flying.
Most witches were skilled herbalists and also utilised the
hallucinogenic properties of this plant in love potions. In folk
medicine, Henbane was used as a pain killer, a remedy for
whooping cough and to treat ulcers and abdominal infections.
In modern medicine it is used in standardised preparations as
an antispasmodic remedy.

Habitat Wasteland
and rubble. On
nutrient-rich soils.
Europe, Asia, northern
Africa.

> *magical plant used by witches*
> *all parts of the plant covered in long shaggy hairs*
> *flowers facing to one side*

petals with dark
grid-pattern

leaf margins
lobed

95

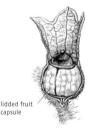

lidded fruit
capsule

Did you know?
*In Hamlet, Shakespeare
quotes the herb 'He-
benon' as the poison
that was used to kill
Hamlet's father. This
is believed to refer to
Henbane. Mediaeval
brewers in Germany
used to add Henbane
to their beer to make it
more intoxicating.*

Jasmine
Jasminum grandiflorum (olive family)
H 4–6m   June–Sept   shrub

Habitat *Originally from the Himalayas, northern India and Pakistan; cultivated in Morocco, Spain and France.*

> climbing plant
> grown as an ornamental garden plant and as a crop plant for the cosmetics industry

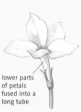

lower parts of petals fused into a long tube

The fragrant essential oil extracted from the flower buds of Jasmine is used primarily in the perfume industry. Eight million flowers are needed for one litre of essential oil! In its country of origin, the flowers are used to make a soothing tea and the oil to treat dry skin. In the West, the oil is used in aromatherapy for its antidepressant qualities, to release tension and anxiety and to strengthen the mind.

sweetly scented flowers

leaves pinnate

Wild Rosemary
Ledum palustre (heather family)
H 60–150cm   May–July   shrub

Habitat *Raised bogs and damp forests. On acidic, lime-free soils. Northern Europe, Asia, North America.*

> evergreen
> leaves alternate
> strongly scented shrub

10 long stamens

The dried herb contains bitter-tasting glycosides and toxic alkaloids. Today it is mainly used in homeopathy, but in former times it was known as a remedy for respiratory diseases, as a sedative and was used to induce abortion. In addition, brewers used the plant as a hop substitute in beer, though this caused an unpleasant kind of drunkenness accompanied by headache and dizziness.

leaves curled down along their edges

underside of leaves rusty-brown, soft

Apple
Malus domestica (rose family)
H up to 10m   May   tree

unripe fruits

As we all know, 'an apple a day keeps the doctor away'! Freshly grated apple is an old household remedy for diarrhoea – apples are a rich source of pectin, which helps regulate digestion. Eaten with the skin on, apples stimulate digestion, help lower cholesterol and blood pressure and act as a depurative. No wonder then that even in Greek mythology the apple already had an important place.

Habitat Only in cultivation, on nutrient-rich soils.

> no thorns – in contrast to the wild form (Crab Apple)
> underside of leaves downy

flowers in clusters

ripe apple

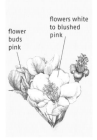

flower buds pink

flowers white to blushed pink

Dwarf Mallow
Malva neglecta (mallow family)
H 15–50cm   June–Oct   annual to biennial

This smaller cousin of the Common Mallow also contains mucilage and, to a lesser extent, tannins. A tea from its leaves helps relieve catarrhs of the respiratory system and soothes painful inflammations of the mucous membranes in mouth and throat and in the gastro-intestinal tract. Ancient references already mention the plant for the same indications.

Habitat Wasteland and disturbed ground, edges of fields, waysides, in gardens. On nutrient-rich soils. Europe, Asia, northern Africa.

> indicates nitrogen-rich soil
> known worldwide as a common weed
> petals twice as long as sepals

petals with dark veins

fruits look like little cheeses

petals up to 15mm long

leaves round, irregularly toothed

Bogbean
Menyanthes trifoliata (bogbean family)
H 15–100cm   May–July   herbaceous perennial

Habitat Shallow margins of lakes and ponds, marshes, bogs, wetland meadows. Europe, Asia, North America.

> thick, branching roots
> flowers in dense clusters on leafless stalks

The flowering herb has traditionally been known as a fever remedy. Modern medicine, however, has not been able to find any active components to confirm this indication. The leaves contain a number of bitter glycosides and alkaloids, which stimulate the digestive glands and thus aid digestion. Folk medicine also utilises the roots as a remedy for stomach complaints, flatulence, rheumatic pain and skin disorders. The plant is contraindicated for gastro-intestinal ulcers.

petals covered in white feathery hairs

flower buds bright pink

leaves trifoliate, on long stalks

flowers up to 15mm in diameter

Health tip
Bogbean tea to stimulate the appetite: use 1 tsp of dried leaves per cup, add boiling water, infuse for 5 minutes, then strain. Alternatively, add cold water and heat to boiling point. Leave to boil for 1 minute, then strain. Drink unsweetened.

Spignel

Meum athamanticum (parsley family)
H 15–45cm   May–June   herbaceous perennial

This plant typically grows in Alpine regions and is therefore known mainly in the local folk medicine of those areas. Probably its most popular application is in the form of a schnapps, known as 'Bärwurz schnapps'. In addition, the root is used in teas to relieve digestive disorders, improve appetite and balance the menstrual cycle.

Habitat Alpine meadows and pastures. On nutrient-poor soils. Central European mountain ranges.

> flowers tiny, 3mm in diameter
> root is used in schnapps
> plant has a spicy fragrance

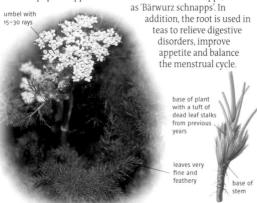

umbel with 15–30 rays

base of plant with a tuft of dead leaf stalks from previous years

leaves very fine and feathery

base of stem

flowers in a compound umbel

❀ 99

Sweet Cicely

Myrrhis odorata (parsley family)
H 60–120cm   May–July   herbaceous perennial

The plant has a strong aniseed scent and its scientific name is derived from the Greek word for perfume. The leaves contain anethole and are a well-known folk remedy in Mediterranean countries. They are used as an expectorant, to aid digestion and to relieve flatulence, and, of course, they also serve as a culinary herb. The root – pickled in alcohol – is taken as a stomachic.

Habitat Mountain meadows, pastures, shrubland and forest margins, above the tree line. Western Alps, Apennines, Pyrenees, also naturalised.

> leaves smell of aniseed when bruised
> seeds with 5 sharp ridges

leaves fern-like

umbel rays covered in soft hairs

compound umbel with numerous rays

Myrtle

Myrtus communis (myrtle family)
H 1–5m   April–Aug   shrub

Habitat *Evergreen forests and shrubland. Mediterranean to north-western Himalayas.*

> **leaves opposite or in threes**
> **berries blueish-black**
> **branches of Myrtle are used as symbols of youth and beauty**

Myrtle has been regarded as a symbol of youth, beauty and virginity since antiquity. For this symbolism it was often used in bridal wreaths. According to Arabic mythology, Adam brought the plant to Earth from the Garden of Eden. The essential oil derived from the leaves has antibacterial properties and is used in medicinal preparations. The dried leaves are used in folk medicine as a remedy for diarrhoea, bladder complaints and respiratory infections.

flower 3cm across

protruding stamens

petals

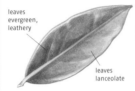

leaves evergreen, leathery

leaves lanceolate

Black Cumin

Nigella sativa (buttercup family)
H 20–40cm   June–Sept   annual

Habitat *Native to western Asia and northern Africa, cultivated in central Europe, occasionally naturalised.*

> **stem upright, branching**
> **leaves pinnate, feathery**

Black Cumin was as popular with the ancient Egyptians as it was with the mediaeval Emperor Charlemagne, who was so fond of this herb that he decreed for it to be cultivated on the imperial farms of his dominions. The black seeds contain a precious aromatic oil – but whether it is of medicinal value remains unconfirmed. Nevertheless, in folk medicine, Black Cumin is prescribed as a remedy for liver complaints, digestive disorders and flatulence.

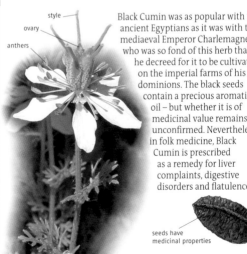

style
ovary
anthers

white or blueish sepals

seeds have medicinal properties

Wood Sorrel

Oxalis acetosella (wood-sorrel family)
H 5–15cm   April–May   herbaceous perennial

The individual leaflets of this plant fold down into a vertical 'sleeping position' during the night. In the morning they spread out to catch the early sunlight, only to fold down again once the sun gets too hot. In folk medicine, the clover-like leaves were used as a remedy for skin conditions, scurvy and as an antidote for arsenic and mercury poisoning. It was held in high repute as a kitchen herb during the reign of Henry VIII, but later lost its position to French Sorrel.

Habitat Mixed deciduous and moist coniferous forests. On shaded ground in temperate regions.

> survives on 1% daylight
> spreads via rhizomes
> flowers solitary on leafless stalks

Health tip

The leaves are not really healthy, since they contain oxalic acid, which is also responsible for their sharp taste. However, a few leaves in salads add a refreshing, tangy flavour and will do no harm in moderation.

petals with fine, purple veins

petals 10–15mm long

101

leaves spread-out in weak light

leaves folded down in bright sunlight

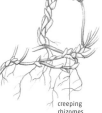

creeping rhizomes

Grass of Parnassus
Parnassia palustris (grass-of-parnassus family)
H 10–25cm   July–Sept   herbaceous perennial

Habitat *Marshes and bogs, near springs. Europe, Asia, North America.*

> *solitary flowers on long stalks*
> *basal leaves in a rosette*

This modest little plant was collected when in flower and then dried. It contains tannins and possibly other, so far unidentified, active components. In folk medicine, it was used to ease nervous disorders such as restlessness, anxiety and palpitations. In addition, there are reports of its application in the treatment of epileptic fits, and some older herbals recommend the plant for liver complaints.

flowers up to 3.5cm across

leaves heart-shaped

stamen

petal

false nectaries

petals with dark veins

Syrian Rue
Peganum harmala (caltrop family)
H 30–60cm   March–Aug   herbaceous perennial

Habitat *Dry wasteland, along waysides. Southern Mediterranean, south-western Asia to Tibet.*

> *herbaceous plant, though woody at base*
> *leaves deeply and irregularly lobed, with 2 stipules*

It is thought that this plant may have been used for ritualistic purposes by some of the earliest human societies. Its seeds contain alkaloids and essential oils and the plant has hallucinogenic as well as aphrodisiac properties. In Mediterranean folk medicine it was used as a remedy for stomach complaints, as a pain killer and to relieve cramps.

flowers 4–5cm in diameter

fruit capsule round, on a long stalk

sepals narrow

petals 1–2cm long

Masterwort

Peucedanum ostruthium (carrot family)

H 30–100cm   June–Aug   herbaceous perennial

The dried root of this plant has a balsamic smell, reminiscent of Angelica or Celeriac. It contains essential oils, tannins and bitter agents. In former times, the plant was used as a remedy for a variety of diseases ranging from gout and rheumatic complaints to bronchitis. In fact, the bitter agents have calmative properties and stimulate the digestive system.

The main active principle in its root, a substance called imperatorin, is a common ingredient in herb schnapps.

Habitat Alpine meadows and pastures, shrubland with Alder, open ground. On well-drained, nutrient-rich soils. European mountain ranges.

> hollow stem
> plant releases aromatic fragrance when bruised
> fruit compressed, winged

leaves biternate

flowers white to pink

root used medicinally

umbel with up to 50 rays

✴ **103**

American Pokeweed

Phytolacca americana (pokeweed family)

H 1–3m   July–Aug   herbaceous perennial   🐛

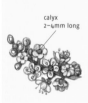

Pokeweed was originally introduced to Europe as an ornamental plant – but winemakers also liked to use the dye from its berries to give a richer colour to their red wines. Native American Indians and European settlers in the New World valued the root as a vulnerary and for the treatment of tumours and skin diseases. A poisonous tincture made from it was taken as a remedy for rheumatism. The berries are only mildly toxic, while the seeds are highly poisonous.

Habitat Vineyards, shrubland, waste ground, along way-sides. Native to North America, but now naturalised worldwide

> base of plant woody
> leaves alternate, lanceolate

berries composed of 10 carpels

calyx 2–4mm long

flowers in a raceme

Aniseed

Pimpinella anisum (parsley family)

H 30–60cm   July–Aug   annual

Habitat Native to eastern Mediterranean, cultivated and naturalised worldwide.

> plant has a distinctive aniseed smell
> stem round, ridged
> upper leaves feathery

A historic herbal from 1577 recommends Aniseed against 'evil-smelling breath'. The plant's essential oil is not only responsible for the characteristic aniseed flavour in sweets and pastries, drinks and mouthwashes, but also has antibacterial properties. Aniseed tea is used in conventional and folk medicine for its expectorant, carminative and antispasmodic properties. In folk medicine, it was also thought to stimulate milk flow in nursing mothers and to enhance sexual desire and performance.

seeds with 5 pale-brown ridges

individual flower 2–3mm across

upper leaves bi- or tri-pinnate

104

umbel with 7–15 rays

Health tip

Aniseed tea as an expectorant: lightly crush the seeds using a pestle and mortar. Use 1/2 tsp per cup of the crushed seeds and add boiling water. Infuse for 10–15 minutes, then strain. Add honey to taste and drink at night before going to bed.

Greater Burnet Saxifrage

Pimpinella major (parsley family)
H 40–100cm   June–Sept   herbaceous perennial

The root of this plant contains essential oils and a number of other active components. It is used in teas or herbal preparations as a remedy for catarrhs of the respiratory system and as a gargle for oral and throat infections. Folk medicine also recommends it as a rinse for slow-healing wounds and as tea for urinary tract infections.

individual flowers 2.5mm in diameter

Habitat Rich meadows and pastures. On deep, nutrient-rich soils. Europe.

> ridged, angular stem
> leaves odd-pinnate
> umbels deflexed before opening

compound umbel with 10–15 smaller umbels

root used medicinally

105

Burnet Saxifrage

Pimpinella saxifraga (parsley family)
H 30–60cm   June–Sept   herbaceous perennial

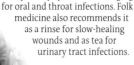

This slightly smaller species contains the same active components as the Greater Burnet Saxifrage. The plant does not grow in the Mediterranean and mediaeval herbalists therefore had no ancient sources to refer to for information about this herb. The first mention of Burnet Saxifrage as a medicinal herb dates from 1588, by the German herbalist Tabernaemontanus, who recommends it for a whole host of diseases.

upper leaves very narrow

flowers white, occasionally pink

Habitat Rough grassland, meadows, moors and heaths, wasteland. On dry, nutrient-poor soils. Europe to central Asia.

> round stem, lightly ridged
> basal leaves pinnate, upper leaves more finely divided

small umbel

individual flowers up to 2mm across

Knotweed

Polygonum aviculare ssp. *aviculare* (knotweed family)

H 5–50cm   May–Nov   annual

Habitat *Common weed on disturbed ground, along roads and on waysides. Worldwide.*

> grows in cracks in roads and pavements
> stem creeping or decumbent
> flowers white to pink

This plant is a very common weed and is so undemanding, it even grows in the cracks of roads and between pavement slabs. The dried shoots contain flavonoids, tannins, mucilage and silicic acid. While the plant has fallen out of use in conventional medicine, folk medicine recommends it, for example, as a remedy for oral and throat infections. Russian Cossacks curiously believed the plant to have aphrodisiac properties.

1–3 flowers in leaf axils

106

leaves sessile or on short stalks

petals 2–3mm long

Health tip

Knotweed tea as a spring tonic: use 1 heaped tbsp of the herb per cup, add cold water and bring to the boil, then strain immediately. Drink 2–3 cups daily for about one month.

leaves oval

branching stem

lateral shoot with flowers

Blackthorn

Prunus spinosa (rose family)

H 1–3m   March–April   shrub

The berries (sloes) on this plant may look ready to eat but eaten raw they are not very palatable. They are best harvested after the first frost and are usually made into jams, jellies, syrups or conserves, or are used as a flavouring in sloe gin and other liqueurs. Sloes are rich in tannins, fruit acids and vitamin C. The flowers are used in a herbal tea with depurative, diuretic and mildly laxative properties. In folk medicine dried sloes are recommended as a stomachic and to help relieve kidney and bladder complaints.

Habitat Hedgerows, forest margins, shrub-land. On nutrient-rich soils. Throughout Europe, western Asia, northern Africa.

> flowers appear in early spring, before the leaves
> fruits provide winter food for birds

Health tip

Sloe juice to boost the appetite: wash the sloes, then add boiling water, cover and leave to stand for 1–2 days. Drain the liquid into another pot and bring to the boil with 500g sugar per 1 litre of sloe juice. Simmer gently to dissolve sugar, then cool. Take a tablespoon before meals.

dwarf shoots terminating in a sharp spike

fruits purplish–blue with a misty bloom

fruits (sloes) resembling plums, but smaller (15mm)

petals up to 8mm long

107

long stamens

Black Currant

Ribes nigrum (gooseberry family)
H 100–200cm   April–May   shrub

Habitat Lowland forests, cultivated in gardens. Europe, Asia.

> **leaves deciduous, palmately lobed**
> **distinctive fragrance**
> **sepals twice as long as petals**

petals greenish–white

Eaten raw, the berries are not really very nice. Black Currant juice, on the other hand, is a popular drink and well known for its healing properties, especially for colds, coughs and oral or throat infections. Chewing the dried berries used to be recommended for infections of the urinary tract. A tea made from Black Currant leaves has a diuretic and diaphoretic action and was thought to relieve liver, gall bladder and rheumatic complaints.

berries in pendant racemes

green, unripe berry

ripe berries deep black

108

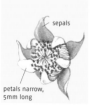

Raspberry

Rubus idaeus (rose family)
H 60–200cm   May–June   shrub

raspberries hollow inside

Habitat Forest glades and paths, rubble and waste ground. On nutrient-rich soils. Northern hemisphere.

> **thorny, arching stems**
> **leaves pinnate, with 3–7 leaflets plus stipules**
> **sepals greenish–white, petals tend to fall off**

The Raspberry, too, is a plant used in folk medicine. The leaves contain tannins, and a tea made from Raspberry leaves is recommended for diarrhoea, to treat oral and throat infections and as a depurative. The leaves are often included in mixed herbal teas, or 'tisanes'. Raspberry juice or syrup is added to other medicines to improve their taste, and the fresh juice is thought to help reduce fever.

sepals

petals narrow, 5mm long

aggregate fruit consisting of a cluster of small drupes

Blackberry

Rubus sect. *Rubus* (rose family)

H 1–4m May–Aug shrub

Blackberry leaf tea has a surprisingly pleasant taste. It is therefore often sold on its own, or the leaves are included in mixed herbal teas. Fermented Blackberry leaves have also in the past been used as a substitute for real tea. The dried leaves are recommended for diarrhoea and can be used in rinses for skin problems or as a gargle for oral and throat infections. Blackberry juice is rich in vitamins and fruit acids.

blackberries initially red, ripe berries black

leaves pinnate, with 3–7 leaflets

sepals spread-out or folded back after flowering

leaves wintergreen

Habitat In hedgerows, shrubland, gardens, forest margins and woodland glades. Northern hemisphere.

> climbs via hooked thorns
> stems biennial, woody
> in many varieties

flowers white to blushed pink, up to 3cm in size

109

Health tip

Blackberry leaf tisane: mix dried Blackberry and Raspberry leaves to equal parts. Add some Lime blossom, dried rosehips and Peppermint leaves for extra flavour. Use 2 tsp of the herb mix per cup, add boiling water, infuse for 10 minutes, then strain.

Elder

Sambucus nigra (honeysuckle family)

H 3–7m   June–July   shrub or small tree

An Elder bush used to be part of every country garden and was thought to ward off evil spirits and protect against witchcraft. Virtually all parts of the plant can be used medicinally.

Elderflower tea has a diaphoretic action and is taken as a remedy for colds, as are the leaves. Elderberry juice is recommended for headaches, constipation and as a diuretic and diaphoretic. The root and bark are said to relieve rheumatic pain. And, according to the great mediaeval scholar Albertus Magnus, the bark, scraped off from the top down, acts as a laxative.

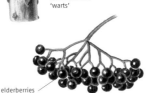

bark with cork 'warts'

umbels 10–25cm across

elderberries 4–6mm in size

Health tip

*Elderflower tea to
ward off colds: use 1
tsp of flowers per cup,
add boiling water and
infuse for 5 minutes,
then strain. Drink se-
veral cups throughout
the day. To induce
sweating, double the
amount of flowers per
cup and drink as hot
as possible.*

110

flowers in a large, flat umbel

Wood Sanicle

Sanicula europaea (parsley family)

H 20–60cm   May–June   herbaceous perennial

flowers white,
occasionally
pink

Wood Sanicle contains saponin compounds, which have expectorant properties. It is recommended for catarrhs of the respiratory system and as a gargle. In the past it was also used as a vulnerary and to treat internal bleeding. Throughout the Middle Ages and beyond, the herb was considered something of an all-heal, as reflected in its name (from Latin sanare = to heal).

leaves
palmately
lobed

leaves mainly
basal

leaves on
long stalks

Habitat Undergrowth
of deciduous and
mixed forests. On
compost-rich soils.
Europe, northern Africa,
western Asia.

> *flowers 2–3mm in size,*
> *white, occasionally pink*
> *fruits with hooked bracts*
> *to aid distribution of*
> *seeds through animals*

small,
globular
umbels

111

Potato

Solanum tuberosum (nightshade family)

H 40–80cm   June–Aug   herbaceous perennial ☠

Like all plants in the nightshade family, the green parts of the Potato plant contain poisonous alkaloids. The tubers, however, are rich in starch and are used as a carrier substance in the pharmaceutical industry. Folk medicine utilised the ability of mashed potatoes to retain heat, in soothing, hot plasters, which were applied to bruises and rheumatic joints.

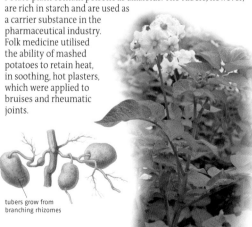

Habitat Native to South
America, cultivated as
a crop and in vegetable
gardens, occasionally
naturalised.

> *green potatoes are*
> *poisonous*
> *leaves odd-pinnate,*
> *leaflets unevenly sized*

flowers 2–3cm
in size

tubers grow from
branching rhizomes

Rowan

Sorbus aucuparia ssp. *aucuparia* (rose family)

H 3–15m   May–June   tree

Habitat Shrubland, mixed and deciduous forests, moors and heaths, hillsides and rocks. Throughout Europe and western Asia.

> grown in varieties as ornamental trees
> berries provide important winter feed for birds
> leaves deciduous, alternate

Eaten raw, Rowan berries are not particularly pleasant. Moreover, they contain active components (sorbic acid and, in the seeds, cyanogenic glycosides), which can irritate the stomach lining. A few raw berries are sometimes utilised as a diuretic and laxative, larger quantities, however, may cause vomiting and diarrhoea. Once cooked, the sorbic acid in the berries is neutralised and they can have the reverse effect. Folk medicine uses Rowan flowers and berries to treat kidney disorders, rheumatic complaints and constipation. The juice can be used as a gargle for laryngitis.

berries
6–9mm in size

up to 100 individual flowers per umbel

leaves pinnate,
leaflets toothed

112

Health tip

Rowanberry jelly: cook the berries with a little water until soft. Strain through a sieve and add sugar to equal parts. Cook until thickened. Take a spoonful of the jelly before meals to stimulate the digestive glands.

leaves
odd-pinnate

Chickweed

Stellaria media (pink family)
H 5–40cm   Jan–Dec   annual

Birds love this plant, and it is often used as a fresh addition to the food of caged birds. The green parts of the plant contain no medicinally active components, but are rich in minerals and vitamin C. Homeopathic preparations of Chickweed are used for rheumatic and liver complaints. In folk medicine it was once well-known as a remedy for itchy skin conditions and pulmonary diseases. An ointment made from Chickweed leaves has been prescribed as a treatment for haemorrhoids.

leaves round to oval

petals 3mm long

Habitat Disturbed ground, in gardens and fields. On nutrient-rich soils. Europe, naturalised worldwide.

> common weed in gardens and fields
> flowers and fruits all year round

5 petals, each with 2 lobes

113

Guelder Rose

Viburnum opulus (honeysuckle family)
H 150–300cm   May–June   shrub

Most Viburnums grown as ornamental shrubs in gardens and parks are introduced exotic species. The wild Guelder Rose, on the other hand, is a common hedgerow plant throughout Britain. Its bark contains tannins and a number of other active components that have yet to be fully analysed. It is known as 'cramp bark' in herbal medicine and is used in homeopathy and conventional medicine to treat cramps and convulsions, including period pain, spasms after childbirth and threatened miscarriage.

Habitat Lowland forests, forest margins, hedgerows, along streams. On nutrient-rich soils. Europe, Asia.

> leaves opposite, maple-like
> flowers in umbels with large sterile flowers on the outside and smaller fertile flowers in the centre
> birds avoid the berries

ripe berries bright red

outer flowers larger, up to 2cm across

umbels up to 10cm in diameter

flowers in a flat umbel

Yarrow

Achillea millefolium (daisy family)

H 20–120cm   Jun–Oct   herbaceous perennial

Habitat *Semi-dry grassland, meadows and pastures, edges of fields. On nutrient-rich soils. Europe, Asia.*

> *numerous tough stems*
> *leaves alternate*
> *capitula combined in an umbel*

disc florets white

ray florets white to pink

The scientific name of this plant refers to Greek mythology: Achilles is said to have used this herb to heal the wounds of his soldiers. And, indeed, an older English name for the plant is 'Soldier's Woundwort'. The dried flowering shoots combine over a hundred active chemicals in a cocktail of healing powers. The herb stimulates the appetite, aids digestion and has anti-inflammatory and antispasmodic properties. Applied externally, Yarrow is used to soothe inflamed skin and mucous membranes. However, in some people, excessive or prolonged use of the herb may cause allergic skin rashes or photosensitivity.

individual capitulum 4–10mm in size

leaves fern-like, finely toothed

Health tip

Yarrow tea to boost the appetite: use 2 tsp of the herb per cup. Add boiling water and leave to infuse for 10 minutes, then strain. Drink in-between mealtimes. To use this as a remedy for stomach or digestive complaints add some Camomile and Peppermint (3:5:5).

Onion

Allium cepa (onion family)

H 60–120cm   June–Aug   herbaceous perennial

Onions are some of the oldest known food and medicinal plants. They contain organic sulphur compounds and are thought to help lower cholesterol and blood pressure. Onions stimulate the appetite and aid digestion. Boiled onion juice with sugar is a traditional household remedy for colds, and the fresh juice is a useful first aid treatment for insect bites.

Habitat *Native to western Asia, cultivated worldwide.*

> *great range of culinary varieties in cultivation*
> *leaves tubular*

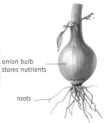

onion bulb stores nutrients

roots

flower head globular

  115

Leek

Allium porrum (onion family)

H 30–100cm   June–July   annual

Whether Leek can be classed as a medicinal plant or not – the Romans certainly seemed to think so. They recommended Leek as a cough remedy, and Emperor Nero is reported to have eaten them to condition his vocal chords. In folk medicine, Leeks are eaten as a remedy for intestinal worms, boiled Leeks are placed on wounds and ulcers, and Leek water is said to aid recovery after severe diarrhoea.

Habitat *Thought to originate from the Mediterranean, mainly in cultivation.*

> *leaves partly tubular, layered*
> *known as a winter vegetable since antiquity*
> *bracts white to pink*

flower head about the size of a tennis ball

leaf base stores nutrients – main edible part of the plant

Garlic

Allium sativum (onion family)

H 20–70cm   June–Aug   herbaceous perennial

Habitat *Native to central Asia, cultivated worldwide, naturalised in sandy soils.*

> flowers with bulbils
> linear leaves, top half of stem leafless

Reports about people who have reached a Methuselah-like age often mention a diet rich in garlic. Sadly, garlic supplements alone are no guarantee for a long life. Nevertheless, a person who smells strongly of garlic can certainly not be accused of eating unhealthily. Garlic aids digestion, lowers cholesterol levels, prevents arteriosclerosis and has strong antiseptic properties. In folk medicine, garlic cloves are used externally to treat warts, corns and eczema.

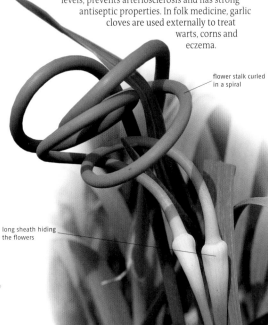

flower stalk curled in a spiral

individual flowers white to pink

116

long sheath hiding the flowers

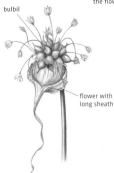

bulbil

flower with long sheath

Health tip

Garlic syrup as a cough remedy: mix 5 crushed garlic cloves with 5 tsp of sugar, add a little water and bring to the boil. Leave for 5 minutes, then strain through a muslin cloth. Take a spoonful of the syrup several times a day.

garlic bulb consisting of individual cloves

Wild Garlic

Allium ursinum (onion family)

H 20–50cm   May–June   herbaceous perennial

The active chemicals of Wild Garlic are the same as those of Garlic, but Wild Garlic is less strongly scented. The whole plant, collected just before coming into flower, is used medicinally. It lowers blood pressure and is used as a household remedy for stomach and digestive complaints, loss of appetite and exhaustion (often together with milk). It is applied in balms, plasters or poultices to treat wounds, eczema and rheumatic joints.

Habitat *Damp woodland, lowland forests, in compost-rich soils. Europe, Asia.*

> *often forms large colonies*
> *strong garlic scent*
> *indicates high groundwater levels*

6 sepals, ca. 1cm long

flowers in a small umbel

narrow bulb

flower stalk leafless

Pellitory

Anacyclus pyrethrum var. *pyrethrum* (daisy family)

H 20–30cm   May–Aug   herbaceous perennial

The English herbalist Nicholas Culpepper (1652) tells us that Pellitory 'is one of the best purges of the brain' and 'an excellent approved remedy in lethargy'. In folk medicine, the root was used to relieve toothache and rheumatic pain, to stimulate saliva flow – and as an aphrodisiac. The plant also grows in India and has a place in Ayurvedic medicine.

Habitat *Mediterranean coastal areas, in cultivation (e.g. in Algeria).*

> *leaves alternate, smooth, pinnate*

ray florets white

disc florets yellow

Catsfoot

Antennaria dioica var. *dioica* (daisy family)
H 10–20cm May–June herbaceous perennial

Habitat Rough grassland, meadows, heaths and moors, pine forests. On mildly acidic soils. Europe, Asia.

> indicator plant for nutrient-poor soil
> male and female flowers on separate plants; male flowers white, female flowers pink

The dried flower heads contain a number of active chemicals – which conventional medicine considers of little use. Nevertheless, folk medicine recommends them in tea as a remedy for liver and gall bladder complaints, diarrhoea and colds, and in some mixed herbal teas they are included for decorative effect.

male flower head

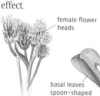

female flower heads

basal leaves spoon-shaped

118

Asparagus

Asparagus officinalis (asparagus family)
H 30–150cm May–July herbaceous perennial

Habitat Thought to originate from the eastern Mediterranean, now widely cultivated, occasionally naturalised in dry and sandy soils.

> Asparagus spears, as sold in the supermarket, are the young shoots of the plant
> fruit is a round red berry
> male and female flowers on separate plants

Asparagus spears grow directly from the rootstock, which contains the plant's active components in much higher concentration than the shoots themselves. Asparagus root has strong diuretic properties and is prescribed as a tea for bladder and kidney infections. Even conventional medications for these conditions often contain some of the active chemicals from Asparagus root.

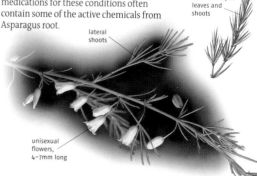

needle-shaped leaves and shoots

lateral shoots

flowers pendant, bell-shaped

unisexual flowers, 4–7mm long

Common Daisy

Bellis perennis (daisy family)

H 5–15cm   Jan–Nov   herbaceous perennial

The humble Common Daisy is mentioned in virtually every major herbal, and is usually described as 'excellent' against all sorts of diseases. Nowadays it is mainly used in homeopathy, where it is indicated for the treatment of bruises and skin conditions. Folk medicine recommends eating the fresh leaves in spring salads, as their bitter agents, flavonoids and essential oils stimulate the metabolism. Externally, the herb is applied to infected wounds, boils, carbuncles and other skin disorders.

Habitat Lawns in gardens and parks, meadows and pastures. On nutrient-rich soils. Throughout most of Europe.

> widespread, on nutrient-rich soils
> tolerates regular mowing
> composite flower on a leafless stalk

ray florets white to pink

leaves in a basal rosette

flower closes at night

numerous disc florets

ray florets 5–10mm long

119

Health tip

Flower water to cleanse oily, blemish-prone skin: place 1 tsp each of daisies (flowers and leaves) and pansies into 1 litre of water. Leave to stand at room temperature over night. Dab the skin with the flower water.

Stemless Carline Thistle

Carlina acaulis ssp. *acaulis* (daisy family)
H 5–60cm   July–Sept   herbaceous perennial

Habitat *Nutrient-poor meadows and pastures, rough grassland, rocky slopes. On alkaline soils. Central and eastern Europe, Alps, mountain ranges in southern Europe.*

> flower head closes in damp weather
> grazing livestock avoids the plant
> capitulum surrounded by bracts, not ray florets

Folk medicine uses the dried root of this plant for its diuretic and diaphoretic properties. It is applied in the treatment of colds and fevers, for stomach complaints and, externally, for wounds and skin conditions. The praise heaped on this plant in some historic herbals, however, may have been a case of mistaken identity: most mediaeval authors used Dioscorides as their source, who, in fact, was referring to a completely different plant.

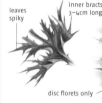

leaves spiky

inner bracts 3–4cm long

capitulum up to 12cm in diameter

disc florets only

120

Roman Camomile

Chamaemelum nobile (daisy family)
H 10–50cm   June–Oct   herbaceous perennial

Habitat *Heaths and acid grassland in Britain. Mediterranean, southern and western Europe, north-western Africa, Azores.*

> traditional herbal remedy
> some cultivars have ray florets only

This plant is also known as English Camomile and is distinguished from German Camomile (*Matricaria recutica*), although both plants have very similar medicinal applications. Camomile has anti-inflammatory and antispasmodic properties. A tea from the dried flowers is recommended for digestive disorders, flatulence, period pain, to calm the nerves and as a rinse for wounds.

leaves bi- or tri-pinnate

capitulum 2–2.5cm across

double flowers of cultivar variety

Lily of the Valley

Convallaria majalis (lily family)
H 10–20cm   May–June   herbaceous perennial ☠

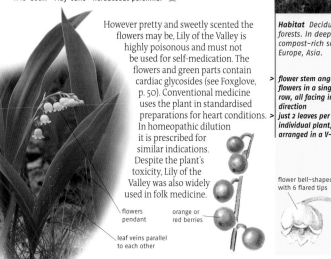

However pretty and sweetly scented the flowers may be, Lily of the Valley is highly poisonous and must not be used for self-medication. The flowers and green parts contain cardiac glycosides (see Foxglove, p. 50). Conventional medicine uses the plant in standardised preparations for heart conditions. In homeopathic dilution it is prescribed for similar indications. Despite the plant's toxicity, Lily of the Valley was also widely used in folk medicine.

flowers pendant

orange or red berries

leaf veins parallel to each other

Habitat *Deciduous forests. In deep, compost-rich soils. Europe, Asia.*

> *flower stem angular, flowers in a single row, all facing in one direction*
> *just 2 leaves per individual plant, arranged in a V-shape*

flower bell-shaped with 6 flared tips

121

Eucalyptus

Eucalyptus globulus ssp. *globulus* (myrtle family)
H up to 40m   Feb–July   tree

leaves curved

Eucalyptus was known to Aboriginal healers as a powerful medicine against fevers and infections. The tree was introduced to Europe as late as the 19th century and therefore lacks the traditional applications of other medicinal plants. Eucalyptus oil has antispasmodic and antibacterial properties, and is particularly effective as an inhalant or in rubs for colds, asthmatic and rheumatic complaints. However, some people have sensitive skin reactions to the oil.

tough, leathery leaves

Habitat *Native to south-eastern Australia and Tasmania, in cultivation in Mediterranean areas. In Britain grown as an ornamental tree.*

> *grown in some areas to drain swamps and thereby eradicate mosquitoes*
> *leaves evergreen*
> *sepals only, no petals*

only stamens are visible

German Camomile
Matricaria recutita (daisy family)
H 15–50cm   May–Aug   annual

Habitat *Along roads and waysides, edges of fields, waste ground. Native to the eastern Mediterranean, naturalised worldwide.*

> *flowers release a distinctive scent when bruised*
> *indicates loamy soil*
> *long heritage as a herbal remedy*

Camomile flowers contain a plethora of active chemicals, which can be utilised individually or as a whole. For once, conventional medicine, homeopathy, folk medicine and the pharmaceutical industry are all in agreement: Camomile is recommended for gastro-intestinal infections, liver and gall bladder complaints, period pain, inflamed mucous membranes and, externally, for skin conditions. It is taken as a tea or inhalant, used in powders or creams and in rinses or baths.

flower head domed and hollow

leaves bi- or tri-pinnate

disc florets

ray florets folded lengthwise

122

Health tip

Camomile tea for stomach and digestive complaints: use 1 heaped tbsp per cup of dried flowers (real Camomile flowers from the herbalist, not teabags from the supermarket!), add boiling water and infuse for 5–10 minutes, then strain. Drink the unsweetened tea lukewarm at intervals between mealtimes.

capitulum 1.5–2.5cm across

Dalmatian Insect Flower
Tanacetum cinerariifolium (daisy family)
H 30–60cm   May–June   herbaceous perennial

The name of this plant refers to the effect of the pyrethrins contained in its flowers and seeds. These substances attack the nervous system of insects and act as a natural insecticide. Although harmful to fish, they are considered safe to use around mammals and birds. In the past, the plant was used to treat intestinal worms and it is still occasionally used as a treatment for head lice and their eggs.

flower head with
disc and ray florets

leaves in clusters
on the ground

Habitat *Open ground, wasteland. Balkans, in the past cultivated in Europe.*

> *plant has an aromatic fragrance*
> *flower heads solitary, white ray florets, yellow disc florets*

capitulum
2–3.5cm in
diameter

 123

Feverfew
Tanacetum parthenium (daisy family)
H 30–60cm   June–Aug   herbaceous perennial

Feverfew leaves are used as a natural insecticide and are applied in poultices for bruises and rheumatic pain. The Romans used the herb to balance the menstrual cycle and also to induce birth – it should not be taken when pregnant! As the English name suggests, Feverfew has traditionally been known as a remedy for headaches and fever. Chewing the fresh leaves is said to be an effective cure for migraine, although this indication is disputed. The leaves may cause allergic reactions and mouth ulcers.

Habitat *Gardens, along waysides, on waste ground. Native to southern Europe (Balkans) and Asia.*

cultivar with
several rings
of ray florets

> *plant is strongly citrus-scented; some find the smell unpleasant*
> *flower heads vary from disc and ray florets to ray florets or disc florets only*

natural form
with disc and
ray florets

capitulum
1.5–2.5cm across

Sea Squill

Urginea maritima (lily family)

H 50–150cm   Aug–Oct   herbaceous perennial

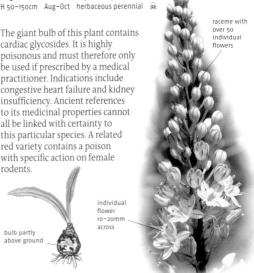

raceme with over 50 individual flowers

Habitat Rocks, dry grassland, garigue, sandy beaches. Mediterranean region only.

> bulb can reach a weight of up to 3kg
> leaves appear long before flowers
> flowers in a tall, upright raceme

The giant bulb of this plant contains cardiac glycosides. It is highly poisonous and must therefore only be used if prescribed by a medical practitioner. Indications include congestive heart failure and kidney insufficiency. Ancient references to its medicinal properties cannot all be linked with certainty to this particular species. A related red variety contains a poison with specific action on female rodents.

flower star-shaped

individual flower 10–20mm across

bulb partly above ground

leaves with several vertical folds

White Hellebore

Veratrum album (lily family)

H 50–150cm   June–Aug   herbaceous perennial

Habitat Alpine meadows and pastures, wet grassland and lowland forests in sub-Alpine regions. Southern European mountain ranges, Asia.

> often forms dense colonies
> leaves oval, wider at base, narrowing at the tip, leaf veins parallel
> petals 10–20mm long

petals with dark veins

The root of White Hellebore contains highly poisonous alkaloids (just 1–2 grams can be fatal!). What makes it even more dangerous is that the plant can easily be mistaken for Yellow Gentian (*Gentiana lutea*). Nevertheless, herbalists in the past were using White Hellebore to treat palpitations, cramps, cholera and fevers, and externally for gout and rheumatic pain. Today it is used only in homeopathy.

flowers in branched spikes, up to 50cm tall

leaves alternate, in staggered whorls

root contains highly poisonous alkaloids

Horse Chestnut
Aesculus hippocastanum (horse chestnut family)
H up to 20m   May–June   tree

While conventional medicine uses mainly the saponin (aescin) contained in the seeds, folk medicine also utilises the leaves, flowers and bark of the Horse Chestnut tree. Aescin, also known as horse chestnut extract, is used in preparations for venous insufficiency, varicose veins, oedema and haemorrhoids. In addition, Horse Chestnut rubs and bath oils are recommended for bruises and to improve circulation. Folk medicine uses the leaves for rheumatic complaints, haemorrhoids, thrombosis and other venous diseases.

Habitat Native to south-eastern Europe (Balkans), widely planted as an ornamental tree in parks and along roads, occasionally naturalised.

> flowers bi- or unisexual
> flowers in upright racemes
> leaflets up to 20cm long

petals 10–15mm long

petals white with a distinct pink mark

125

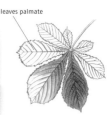

leaves palmate

fruit shell with short spikes

seed ('conker')

Health tip
Horse Chestnut preparations are available for most of the plant's main indications. This is a traditional household remedy: use a tincture of Horse Chestnut leaves, flowers and bark soaked in brandy as a rub to ease rheumatic pain.

Bear's Breeches
Acanthus mollis (acanthus family)
H 50–120cm   March–June   herbaceous perennial

Habitat Waste ground, shrubland, garigue. Mediterranean region, popular garden plant throughout Europe.

> leaves used as a motif in Corinthian architecture
> black, branching taproot

The leaves of this plant are thought to have been the design inspiration for the Corinthian column capitals created by the Greek sculptor Callimachus in the 5th century BC. Not much later, the plant is first mentioned as a medicinal herb. Nowadays, the plant is used in folk medicine only. Its leaves are applied externally to treat burns and sprains and taken in teas or tinctures to relieve flatulence, colic and nervous disorders.

flower spikes up to 1m tall

corolla up to 4cm

basal leaves up to 1m long

126

Lemon Verbena
Aloysia triphylla (vervain family)
H 100–250cm   Aug–Sept   shrub

Habitat Originally from South America, introduced to Europe as an ornamental plant.

> leaves release a strong citrus scent when bruised
> leaves usually in whorls of three

flower white to pale purple

The dried leaves contain essential oils, mucilage and other substances. They are a popular household remedy, especially in France, where they are taken as a tea against digestive disorders, insomnia and anxiety. The pure essential oil is used in perfumes. The leaves are often added to mixed herbal teas for their refreshing citrus flavour.

corolla 2-lipped

leaves lanceolate, pointed

Eyebright

Euphrasia officinalis ssp. *rostkoviana* (figwort family)

H 5–45cm   May–Oct   annual

corolla 15mm long

The herb contains a number of active components, although its application in folk medicine was most probably based on the Doctrine of Signatures. The flower was thought to resemble a human eye and the plant was therefore indicated for the treatment of eye infections and to soothe and refresh tired eyes. In addition, it is recommended for coughs, colds and stomach complaints. Plants collected in the wild should not be used, as they pose a risk of infection.

Habitat *Rough grassland, meadows and pastures in mountainous regions, blanket bogs. On lime-free soils. Europe.*

> *stem covered in coarse, glandular hairs*
> *flowers in upper leaf axils*

leaves oval, coarsely toothed

upper petals helmet-shaped

lower petals with a yellow patch

127

Goat's Rue

Galega officinalis (pea family)

H 60–120cm   June–Aug   herbaceous perennial

The plant contains a substance called galegin, which has been shown in laboratory tests to reduce blood sugar levels. However, conventional medicine favours more established medication to treat diabetes. Furthermore, galegin molecules are chemically very similar to the poisonous substance guanidine. In folk medicine, Goat's Rue is used as a diuretic and to promote milk flow in nursing mothers.

Habitat *Native to the eastern Mediterranean, naturalised on wasteland sites, along roads and railway embankments.*

> *flowers white to pale violet*
> *leaves odd-pinnate; leaflets sharply pointed*

flower 1cm long

cylindrical seed pods

leaves with 7–19 leaflets

flower stalk longer than the leaf below

Soya Bean
Glycine max (pea family)
H 30–100cm   July–Aug   annual

Habitat *Native to eastern Asia, cultivated worldwide as a crop plant.*

> *known only in cultivated form*
> *flowers white to pale pink*
> *leaves on long stalks, trifoliate*

Soya Bean oil is not just a cooking ingredient but also a pharmaceutical substance. In creams and balms it serves as a carrier oil for other substances; if taken as part of a controlled diet it can help lower cholesterol levels; and it contains estrogenic substances that are said to ease the symptoms of the menopause, help prevent osteoporosis and heart disease, and possibly even protect against cancer – although these claims are not universally accepted.

leaves trifoliate

corolla 6–8mm long

oil is derived from the seeds within the Soya Beans

128

Hedge Hyssop
Gratiola officinalis (figwort family)
H 20–40cm   April–Aug   herbaceous perennial

Habitat *Meadows, near water. On wet, peaty soils. Asia, Europe.*

> *plant glabrous*
> *leaves opposite, sessile*
> *flowers on stalks in upper leaf axils*

All parts of this plant are highly poisonous and the herb is not suitable for self-medication. However, in the past it was widely used by herbalists as a strong purgative and as a remedy for gout and liver complaints. Externally, the dried herb was applied in poultices to treat skin diseases.

corolla up to 15mm long

leaves sessile, finely toothed

flowers white to purple

White Dead-nettle

Lamium album (mint family)
H 20–50cm   April–Oct   herbaceous perennial

When not in flower, the plant bears a strong resemblance to the Stinging Nettle, though it has no stinging hairs. The flowers and leaves were once a popular household remedy and the plant is still used in modern herbal medicine as well as in homeopathy. Dead-nettle tea is recommended for catarrhs of the respiratory system, stomach and digestive complaints, bloating and flatulence. Externally, it was used in compresses and rinses for skin infections and to relieve period pain.

Habitat Waysides, ditches, hedgerows, forest margins, gardens. Widespread in Europe and Asia.

> indicates nitrogen-rich soils
> labiate flowers in whorls in the leaf axils
> leaves opposite

corolla 2–3cm long

calyx with 5 long, thin spikes

129

leaves coarsely toothed, no stinging hairs

flowers in whorls

leaves decussate

Health tip

Dead-nettle tea as a natural sedative and sleep aid: use 1–2 tsp of Dead-nettle flowers per cup. Add cold water and bring to the boil. Leave to infuse for 5 minutes, then strain. Sweeten with honey and drink immediately.

Gipsywort

Lycopus europaeus (mint family)

H 20–130cm   July–Sept   herbaceous perennial

Habitat Water's edge, reedbeds, ditches. On damp and wet ground. Europe, Asia, northern Africa.

> labiate flowers in whorls in the leaf axils
> leaves opposite, toothed or deeply lobed

The plant's active components influence the balance of hormones in the body, and this property is utilised in the treatment of overactive thyroid and premenstrual syndrome by both herbal and conventional medicine. In folk medicine, Gipsywort was known as a remedy for fever and was used to stem bleeding and clean wounds.

corolla 4–6mm long

lower petals with dark red markings

leaves lanceolate

130

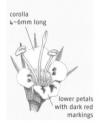

White Horehound

Marrubium vulgare (mint family)

H 40–50cm   June–Aug   herbaceous perennial

Habitat Waysides, on walls, rubble, in gardens. Mediterranean region, Britain.

> entire plant covered in hoary down
> labiate flowers in round, nest-shaped whorls
> leaves 'wrinkly'

White Horehound is one of the oldest known medicinal plants – its scientific name is thought to be derived from Hebrew. The dried herb is commonly used in Mediterranean countries as a remedy for loss of appetite, stomach and digestive complaints, bloating and flatulence, respiratory catarrhs and, externally, as a treatment for wounds. It should not be used, however, if suffering from gastro-intestinal ulcers.

flowers in leaf axils

flowers 6–7mm long

calyx with 10 hooked teeth

leaves crenate to serrate

Lemon Balm

Melissa officinalis (mint family)
H 20–80cm   June–Aug   herbaceous perennial

This plant is used in medicines, balms and mixed herbal teas. Lemon Balm is recommended for nervous disorders, stomach and digestive complaints and mild heart conditions; it has antispasmodic and calmative properties, relieves insomnia and eases rheumatic pain. A spirit of Lemon Balm, combined with lemon-peel, nutmeg and Angelica root, known as 'Carmelite Water', used to be a popular remedy for nervous headaches and neuralgic affections.

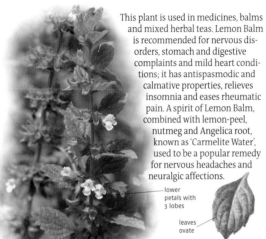

lower petals with 3 lobes

leaves ovate

Habitat Native to the eastern Mediterranean and south-western Asia, cultivated in England for over 1000 years and widely naturalised.

> distinctive lemon scent
> labiate flowers, all facing to one side
> flowers white to yellow

corolla 8–15mm long

Curly Spearmint

Mentha spicata ssp. *crispa* (mint family)
H 30–100cm   July–Sept   herbaceous perennial

The leaves contain a complex essential oil, which is responsible for the plant's characteristic scent and its medicinal properties. It is widely used in the production of toothpaste, mouthwash and chewing gum. The leaves have traditionally been known to relieve flatulence, aid digestion and improve the appetite. The essential oil is used as an inhalant in the treatment of colds.

flowers in terminal spikes

leaves curly

branching stem

Habitat Origins uncertain, only known from cultivation as a medicinal and culinary herb, though often naturalised.

> branching plant
> leaves opposite, margins raggedly toothed
> flowers white to pale pink

flowers in dense spikes, individual flowers with long stamens

French Bean

Phaseolus vulgaris (pea family)

H 30cm–4m   June–Sept   annual   ☠

Habitat *Originally from Central and South America. Cultivated worldwide as a vegetable.*

> shrub or climbing varieties
> flowers white to pale violet
> uncooked beans are poisonous

All parts of this plant are poisonous, even the dried pods, although the level of toxicity depends on the variety. Teas and other preparations from the seed pods are used as a diuretic in both conventional and folk medicine. Herbalists used to recommend the beans – perhaps for the chromium picolinate they contain – in the treatment of diabetes, gout and acne.

petals 10–15mm long

flowers in loose racemes

seed pods smooth

leaves trifoliate

Fenugreek

Trigonella foenum-graecum (pea family)

H 10–50cm   June–July   annual

Habitat *In cultivation in southern Europe, native to south-western Asia.*

> long taproot
> seeds have an intense, slightly unpleasant fragrance
> petals yellowish-white

Records show that Fenugreek seeds were already held in high esteem by ancient Egyptian and Arabic physicians. The plant was introduced to northern Europe in the early Middle Ages, around the time of Emperor Charlemagne. The spicy and bitter-tasting herb is eaten as a remedy for loss of appetite and applied in poultices for skin eruptions. The seeds are recommended for catarrhs and diabetes.

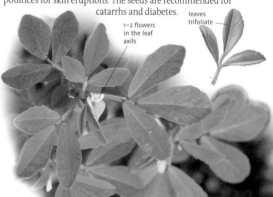

leaves trifoliate

1–2 flowers in the leaf axils

petals 10–18mm long

Common Vervain

Verbena officinalis (vervain family)

H 30–100cm   July–Sept   annual to herbaceous perennial

The name Vervain is thought to be derived from the Celtic ferfaen, meaning 'to drive away stones' – the plant was used in the treatment of bladder stones. In fact, in mediaeval times it was used for a whole range of diseases and was also believed to protect against witchcraft. Modern medicine, however, is less enthusiastic about the herb. It contains glycosides, flavonoids and essential oils and is said to stimulate milk flow, act as a diuretic and a remedy for oral and throat, gastro-intestinal and urinary tract infections. In Bach flower remedies, Vervain is recommended for those who find it hard to relax and are unable to take advice from others.

Habitat Wasteland, meadows, along waysides, on walls. Widespread. Europe (except northern Europe), northern Africa, south-western Asia.

> **flowers white to pale purple**
> **stem 4-sided, angular**

flowers vaguely labiate

flowers in slender spikes

corolla 3–5mm long

133

upper leaves sessile

lower leaves stalked

Health tip

Vervain tea to settle the stomach: use 1 heaped tsp of the dried herb per cup, add boiling water, infuse for 5 minutes, then strain. Drink immediately.

Devil's Bit Scabious

Succisa pratensis (teasel family)

H 15–80cm   July–Sept   herbaceous perennial

Habitat *Fens and wetlands, Alpine meadows, damp, nutrient-poor grassland. On nutrient-poor soils. Central Europe, western Asia.*

> **leaves in a basal rosette**
> **upper leaves opposite**
> **root looks 'bitten-off'**

flowers in a spherical capitulum

The plant's name refers to its root, which stops abruptly as if bitten off – out of spite by the devil, as legend has it. It is now only used in homeopathy and folk medicine, but in the past it was well known for its expectorant and depurative properties, as a remedy for coughs and sore throats, and was applied in poultices to bruises and skin eruptions.

capitulum up to 3cm in diameter

root with medicinal properties

Brooklime

Veronica beccabunga (figwort family)

H 20–60cm   May–Aug   herbaceous perennial

Habitat *Along streams and ditches, reedbeds, near springs. On moist ground and floodplains. Europe, Asia, northern Africa.*

> **flowers in clusters on long, opposite stalks**
> **stem prostrate or decumbent**

petals not quite symmetrical

In former times, the leaves of this plant were eaten in salads as a depurative and to prevent scurvy. The dried flowering herb was used to stimulate the appetite, as a diuretic and laxative, and was taken as a remedy for bladder stones, rheumatic complaints, skin disorders and gingivitis. In modern herbal medicine its use has become largely obsolete.

leaves opposite

leaves thinly fleshy

flowers 6–8mm in size

Common Speedwell

Veronica officinalis (figwort family)

H 10–20cm   June–Aug   herbaceous perennial

The heydays of Common Speedwell as a medicinal herb were during the Middle Ages, when it was considered something of an all-heal. In folk medicine, the herb is still used as a remedy for colds, digestive complaints, rheumatism and as a diuretic. Speedwell tea is said to relieve hot flushes during the menopause and is used as a gargle to soothe oral and throat infections.
In modern herbalism it is no longer much used, though it is prescribed in homeopathy for the treatment of eczema and bronchitis.

leaves oval, on short stalks

Habitat Heaths, rough grassland, forest clearings, along waysides. On sandy and stony ground. Europe, western Asia.

> *prefers acidic soils*
> *only upper part of stem upright*
> *stems downy*

petals with dark veins

135

petals not quite symmetrical

flowers in one-sided racemes

Health tip

For a soothing bath, place a handful of Speedwell leaves into a saucepan with 1 litre of water, bring to the boil, strain and add to bathwater. Relax in the bath for up to 20 mins.

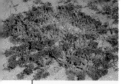

Alkanet

Alkanna tuberculata (borage family)
H 10–30cm   April–June   herbaceous perennial

upper leaves sessile

Habitat *Rocky and sandy coasts, waste ground. Mediterranean region, in central Europe as a garden plant.*

> **stem prostrate or decumbent**
> **leaves narrow, base of upper leaves heart-shaped**

The root of this plant contains a red dye, which was used in the past as a food colouring and in cosmetics. It has astringent properties and used to be taken as a remedy for diarrhoea or was applied to skin conditions. However, it contains pyrrolizidine alkaloids, which can damage the liver and may even cause cancer. The herb is therefore no longer considered safe for internal use.

flower 6–8mm in diameter

petals fused at base

root contains red dye

leaves and stem downy

Columbine

Aquilegia vulgaris (buttercup family)
H 40–80cm   May–July   herbaceous perennial

Habitat *Open deciduous forests, shrubland, meadows, hedgerows and gardens. Europe, Asia, northern Africa.*

> **common garden plant, available in a variety of flower colours**
> **leaves biternate**

The plant is poisonous when fresh, although the toxins are destroyed through heat or drying. Grazing animals avoid the plant. In homeopathy, Columbine is prescribed for nervous disorders and irregular periods. In folk medicine it was used to treat skin rashes as well as liver, gall bladder and gastro-intestinal complaints. It is no longer used in modern herbal medicine.

flowers nodding, up to 5cm long

petals with long spurs

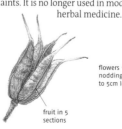

fruit in 5 sections

Borage
Borago officinalis (borage family)
H 20–80cm   May–Sept   annual

The oil extracted from the seeds of this plant (also known as star-flower oil) is widely sold as a herbal supplement and is thought to be effective in regulating the menstrual cycle, lowering blood pressure and cholesterol as well as helping to reduce inflammation and improve mobility of the joints. The use of the green herb, however, is no longer advised.

Habitat Native to the Mediterranean, naturalised throughout Europe and Britain.

> plant smells of cucumber
> covered in stiff, bristly hairs
> upper leaves decurrent

flowers 2–3cm across

leaves ovate

sepals hairy

anthers fused into a column

Common Flax
Linum usitatissimum (flax family)
H 30–60cm   June–July   annual

Flax is one of the oldest crop plants in human history. In ancient Egypt it was grown for fibre and as a medicinal plant. The seeds are high in mucilage, which swells considerably in the digestive tract, thereby acting as a mild laxative. Linseed poultices are used to treat skin diseases. The mediaeval herbalist Hildegard von Bingen also recommended it for burns and scalds.

flowers sky blue

Habitat Thought to originate from the Mediterranean. Widely cultivated, occasionally naturalised.

> cultivated since Neolithic times
> leaves narrow, alternate
> flowers in branching panicles of up to 10 flowers

flowers 2–3cm in diameter

seed capsule

Autumn Mandrake
Mandragora autumnalis (nightshade family)
H 10–20cm   Sept–Nov   herbaceous perennial

Habitat *Along waysides, on open ground in Mediterranean regions.*

> **stem short and stubby**
> **flowers on short stalks, blueish purple**
> **yellow-orange berries**

The Mandrake, or Mandragora, has always been more associated with magic and witchcraft than with medicine. Nevertheless, references to the plant date back as far as the famous Egyptian Ebers papyrus of 1550 BC, and continue throughout ancient Greek, Roman and mediaeval writings. The peculiar shape of its root, which was thought to resemble a human body, may have been responsible for the many superstitions surrounding the plant, including its use in amulets to ward off all sorts of evil. The root contains poisonous alkaloids and is used as a narcotic and for pain relief.

bell-shaped flower

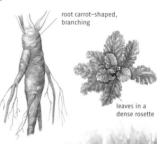

root carrot-shaped, branching

leaves in a dense rosette

Did you know?
According to mediaeval folklore, the Mandrake root would utter a terrible shriek when dug up, which would kill anyone who heard it. Therefore, a dog was used to dig out the plant whilst the noise from the Mandrake was drowned out by blowing a loud horn.

138

flower 4–5cm in size

leaves oblong, 'wrinkly' and leathery

Woody Nightshade

Solanum dulcamara (nightshade family)

H 30–200cm   June–Aug   shrub   ☠

Herbalists used to prescribe the stems and young shoots of this plant as a diuretic and laxative and as a remedy for nausea, chronic bronchitis, asthma and skin diseases. It contains poisonous alkaloids and is now only used in homeopathy and in standardised preparations for the treatment of eczema.

Habitat Along ditches, near water, shrubland, lowland forests. On damp and wet ground. Europe, Asia, northern Africa.

> stem with a woody base
> trailing or twining

petals fused, with 5 star-shaped lobes

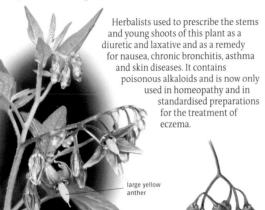

large yellow anther

bright red, egg-shaped berries

Lesser Periwinkle

Vinca minor (periwinkle family)

H 15–20cm   April–May   herbaceous perennial   ☠

Periwinkle contains an alkaloid called vincamin, which is used in pharmaceutical preparations as a cerebral stimulant and vasodilator to improve blood flow to the brain and inner ear. In folk medicine, the plant was used as a gargle, it was applied externally to bruises and eczema, and was also thought to improve brain function and memory. Self-medication is not recommended.

Habitat Deciduous forests. On nutrient-rich soils. Europe, western Asia. Common garden plant, also naturalised.

> evergreen
> creeping stem, forming new roots at the nodes

leaves opposite

flower 2–3cm across

petals not quite symmetrical

Cornflower

Centaurea cyanus (daisy family)

H 30–60cm   June–Oct   annual

Habitat *Cornfields, wasteland, disturbed ground. Prefers sandy soils. Originally from the western Mediterranean.*

> once a common agricultural weed – now listed as an endangered plant species in the UK
> solitary flower heads
> stem covered in white down

The pretty, deep-blue flowers are sometimes added to herbal tea mixes. Cornflower used to be a widespread weed in arable fields, but has become rare as a result of modern agricultural practice. In the days before chemical herbicides, the plant was a common household remedy for digestive complaints and loss of appetite, and was used as an expectorant, a mouth- and eyewash and to treat dandruff.

capitulum 2.5–3.5cm across

underside of leaves downy

outer florets enlarged

Common Chicory

Cichorium intybus (daisy family)

H 30–150cm   July–Oct   herbaceous perennial

root used as coffee substitute

Habitat *Road verges and waysides, waste ground, railway embankments. On nutrient-rich soils. Europe, Asia.*

> loosely branching plant
> plant releases a milky sap when bruised
> flowers open in the morning and close by midday

In the past, roasted Chicory root was used as a caffeine-free coffee substitute. It also has a high inulin content and can be processed into a sweetener. In addition, it is used as a diuretic, to boost the appetite and to aid digestion. In Bach flower remedies, Chicory is recommended for parents who are possessive and overprotective of their children.

lower half of leaves deeply lobed

capitulum 3–5cm in diameter

stiff, angular stems

clear blue ray florets only

Saffron

Crocus sativus (iris family)

H 10–30cm   Sept–Nov   bulb   ☠

The saffron threads used in cookery are, in fact, the dried styles of the Saffron flower, which divide into three orange-coloured stigmas. Although the whole plant is poisonous, the small quantities used in cooking are perfectly safe. In homeopathic doses it is used to treat cramps, nosebleeds and depression. Saffron stimulates the uterus and larger quantities of it have been used to induce abortion – often with fatal consequences. Avoid Saffron if pregnant, even as a spice.

Habitat Thought to originate from southern Europe, wild form not known. Cultivated primarily in Spain.

> **flower tube downy**
> **leaves narrow, with a central, vertical white line**

6 petals, fused at base, forming a long tube

141

leaves narrow, like blades of grass

petals with dark veins

3 rusty red stigmas

saffron as sold for culinary use

Did you know?

Saffron is to this day the world's most expensive spice: 20,000 flowers are needed to yield 100 grams of the spice. The saffron threads can only be picked by hand, as no machine is able to harvest the delicate styles.

Cardoon
Cynara cardunculus (daisy family)
H 50–150cm   April–Aug   biennial

Habitat *Originally from the Mediterranean or Ethiopia, cultivated throughout the Mediterranean region.*

> wild form of the globe artichoke
> leaves simple or deeply lobed

The large fleshy flower buds of this plant are eaten as a vegetable, while the basal leaves, collected before the plant comes into flower, are used as a herbal remedy. *Cynara* extract is prescribed to improve liver function and stimulate the digestive glands. In Mediterranean regions, the juice of the plant is mixed with wine and taken as a liver tonic.

disc florets only

large bracts below the capitulum

fleshy, edible bracts

capitulum up to 15cm in diameter

Hepatica
Hepatica nobilis var. *nobilis* (buttercup family)
H 5–15cm   March–April   herbaceous perennial

Habitat *Beech and Oak forests. On well-drained, loamy soils. Europe, except western Europe.*

> indicates alkaline soils
> solitary flowers, 3.5cm in size
> leaves wintergreen, appear after flowering

The fresh green plant is poisonous and is now used only in homeopathy in the treatment of bronchitis, throat infections and liver complaints. The leaves are liver-shaped and in the past the plant was recommended, according to the Doctrine of Signatures, as a remedy for 'blocked' liver and all kinds of liver, kidney and bladder problems.

flowers 1.5–3.5cm across

leaves and flowers on long stalks

5–10 petals

leaves broad, in 3 lobes

shiny leaves

Flag Iris

Iris germanica (iris family)

H 30–100cm   May–June   herbaceous perennial

Flag Iris, or Blue Flag, has been grown since antiquity for its medicinal properties as much as for its magnificent flowers. Emperor Charlemagne had the plant grown in his provinces and it was one of the plants grown in the famous monastic gardens of Walafrid Strabo at the Abbey of Reichenau on Lake Constance. The root is used for its expectorant properties as a remedy for coughs and colds, and is also said to relieve flatulence, nausea and to improve circulation. .

Habitat Naturalised garden plant, thought to originate from the eastern Mediterranean.

> 3–5 flowers per plant on short stalks
> 3 petals upright, 3 folded down

short, stubby root

inner petals upright

petals up to 8cm long

143

outer petals with a yellow 'beard'

basal leaves sword-shaped

Did you know?

The dried root is known as 'orris root' and is used in perfumery and as an ingredient in toothpastes and breath fresheners. In the past, sections of the dried root were given to teething infants to chew on. However, this practice is no longer advised due to the risk of bacterial infections from micro-organisms on the root.

Monkshood

Aconitum napellus (buttercup family)

H 50–150cm   June–Aug   herbaceous perennial   ☠

Monkshood is extremely poisonous – even more so as its poison, aconitine, can be absorbed through mere contact with the skin or the mucous membranes. Cases of death through aconite poisoning – intentional and unintentional – have been recorded since antiquity. Even mediaeval herbalists were very cautious in the application of this plant. The root is used occasionally in modern medicine and in homeopathy, where Aconite is prescribed for fever, inflammation, bronchitis, neuralgia and heart conditions.

Habitat *Damp shady places and moist rich meadows in southern Wales and south-western England. Mountain ranges of southern and central Europe.*

> **root thick and tuberous**
> **flower helmet-shaped, as wide as tall**
> **grows in moist, nutrient-rich soils**

upper petal helmet-shaped

flower dark purple or deep blue

144

2 nectaries hidden within the flower hood

flower shown without the hood

anthers and stigmas

upper leaves sessile

deeply lobed

stem very straight and upright

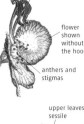

flowers in tall, single or branching racemes

Did you know?

The symptoms of aconite poisoning occur within minutes, in the form of burning, tingling, and numbness in the mouth, hot and cold sweats, nausea and vomiting. The mind remains clear throughout. Call emergency services immediately and try to induce vomiting.

Bugle

Ajuga reptans (mint family)

H 10–30cm   May–Aug   herbaceous perennial

flowers in 2–6 in the leaf axils

Although not much used in modern medicine, Bugle has a long history as a wound herb and a household remedy for liver and gall bladder complaints as well as oral and throat infections. It is collected as it comes into flower in late spring. In fact, purists say that its medicinal powers are at its best if harvested before sunrise during a new moon.

Habitat *Meadows and lawns, shrubland, forests. Widespread. Northern hemisphere.*

> *stem square, angular, smooth on 2 sides, downy on the other 2*
> *flowers in broad spikes*
> *spreads through runners*

leaves opposite, margins entire

upper petals very short

flower 10–15mm long

Forking Larkspur

Consolida regalis (buttercup family)

H 20–40cm   May–Aug   annual ☠

Although the plant contains poisonous alkaloids, their concentration is relatively low in the flowers, which were used in folk medicine as a diuretic and depurative. They are still sometimes included as a decorative element in mixed herbal teas.

flower 3–4cm in diameter

Habitat *Arable fields, along waysides. On nutrient-rich, alkaline soils. Throughout most of Europe, western Asia.*

> *casual agricultural weed*
> *spur 15–30mm long, with nectaries*

leaves deeply dissected, leaflets linear

flower with long spur

Stavesacre
Delphinium staphisagria (buttercup family)
H 30–100cm   May–Aug   annual

Habitat *Evergreen shrubland, disturbed ground. Mediterranean region.*

> **stem and leaves hairy**
> **flowers in tall, loosely branching racemes**

short spur, 3–4mm long

petals 15–20mm long

This plant is a relative of Forking Lark-spur, though the dried seeds, rather than the flowers, are used medicinally. They, too, contain toxic alkaloids and have been used in pain killers and antispasmodic medications. In the past, they were chewed to relieve toothache and gum disease, and their toxicity was utilised in the treatment of head lice – an older name of the plant is 'Licebane'.

centre of flower pale

leaves palmate, on long stalks

Moldavian Dragonhead
Dracocephalum moldavicum (mint family)
H 30–70cm   July–Aug   annual

Habitat *Originally from Siberia and the Himalayas, grown as a crop plant in central and eastern Europe.*

> **plant has an aromatic fragrance, similar to Lemon Balm**
> **flowers in dense spikes**

labiate flower, 2cm long

The plant was introduced to Europe via Constantinople, as late as the 16th century, and is therefore not listed in ancient or mediaeval sources. The dried plant is used as a culinary and medicinal herb (similar to Lemon Balm). It has calmative and antispasmodic properties and aids digestion.

flowers in whorls

leaves in threes, coarsely toothed

Ground Ivy

Glechoma hederacea (mint family)

H 10–40cm April–June herbaceous perennial

Ground Ivy has been a popular folk remedy throughout history. The early Saxons used it to clarify their beer and improve its flavour. In fact, it was still used for this purpose until the reign of Henry VIII. In herbal medicine it was used to treat throat and chest infections, digestive complaints and fever. The 16th century English herbalist John Gerard recommends Ground Ivy for headaches, saying that 'it purgeth the head from rheumatic humours flowing from the brain'. Externally it was used in poultices and rinses for slow-healing wounds and other skin problems.

__Habitat__ Meadows, lowland forests, forest margins, hedgerows. On nutrient-rich soils. Europe, Asia.

> *colonising plant*
> *evergreen*
> *stem creeping, forming roots at the nodes*

upper leaves often with a reddish tint

flower 10–22mm long

147

stem square, angular

leaves heart-shaped, coarsely toothed

lower petals with dark pattern

Health tip

Ground Ivy tea for stomach complaints and loss of appetite: use 1–1 1/2 tsp of the dried flowering shoots per cup, add boiling water and infuse for 5 minutes. Strain and drink the tea immediately.

Viper's Bugloss

Echium vulgare (borage family)

H 25–100cm   May–July   biennial

Habitat *Waysides, wasteland and rubble, on disturbed ground. On well-drained soils. Europe, Asia Minor, north-western Africa.*

> basal rosette only in year one
> flower spike up to 50cm tall
> stamens and style protruding from the corolla

On account of the shape of its flowers, which were thought to resemble a snake's head, the 17th century English herbalist William Coles recommends Viper's Bugloss as an antidote to snake poison. In central European folk medicine, the dried root was used as a cure for epilepsy and to treat slow-healing wounds.

flowers reminiscent of a viper's head

stem covered in coarse glandular hairs

corolla up to 2cm long

148

Hyssop

Hyssopus officinalis ssp. *officinalis* (mint family)

H 20–80cm   July–Oct   herbaceous perennial

Habitat *Rocky ground and rubble, garigue. Mediterranean and Black Sea regions.*

> dwarf shrub, lower parts woody
> aromatic fragrance
> leaves with oil glands

Hyssop is referred to in the Bible, where the herb is used to cleanse leprosy sufferers. In folk medicine it was used as a remedy for throat infections and hoarseness as well as for many other diseases, from asthma to eye infections to circulatory problems. The essential oil contained in Hyssop is very powerful and the plant should only be taken in small doses.

flowers 7–12mm long

flowers in a one-sided raceme

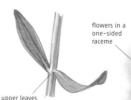

upper leaves sessile

Common Lavender

Lavandula angustifolia ssp. *angustifolia* (mint family)

H 50–100cm   July–Sept   shrub

Anyone who has ever walked among the rows and rows of
lavender in the French Provence – and has seen the abundance of
lavender-related products in the local souvenir shops – is unlikely
to ever forget this plant. A tea from lavender flowers is said to
stimulate the appetite, settle the stomach, calm the nerves and
help promote sleep. Lavender cushions are often used as a subtle
sleep aid. The purified essential oil is one of the most popular
aromatherapy oils and is used in perfumes, soaps and bath oils.

Habitat *Rocky ground,
garigue. Native to
southern Europe.
Commonly grown
as a garden and
ornamental shrub.*

> **compact, aromatically
scented shrub**
> **flowers in whorled spikes
on long stalks, rising tall
above the shrub itself**

flowers
in whorled
terminal spikes

young
leaves
downy

small labiate
flowers, about
10–12mm long

Health tip

*For a soothing
lavender bath, add
50–60 grams of
lavender flowers to 1
litre of water. Bring to
the boil, then leave to
settle for 10 minutes.
Strain and add to your
bathwater. Relax in
the bath and go to
bed afterwards.*

149

Spike Lavender
Lavandula latifolia (mint family)
H 50–100cm   July–Sept   shrub

Habitat *Evergreen shrubland, maquis. Southern Europe to Balkans.*

> *compact, low-growing shrub, strong, aromatic fragrance*
> *bracts lanceolate*

The medicinal properties of Spike Lavender are similar to those of Common Lavender. Although the flowers yield more essential oil, it is considered of inferior quality and less fragrant than that of Common Lavender. It is used externally to treat wounds, burns and rheumatic pain; added to a steam inhalation bath it soothes catarrhs of the respiratory system; and a drop of Lavender oil on a spoonful of sugar is said to aid digestion.

flowers in spikes

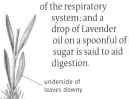

underside of leaves downy

small labiate flower, 8–10mm long

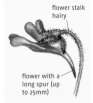

Common Butterwort
Pinguicula vulgaris (bladderwort family)
H 5–15cm   May–June   herbaceous perennial

Habitat *Bogs, near springs, on wet ground. Europe, Asia, North America.*

> *carnivorous plant*
> *leaves sticky, in a basal rosette*

This plant is able to trap insects, which it then digests in order to supplement its supply of nutrients. This enables it to succeed in soils that are deficient in nitrogen. In the past, the plant was considered a remedy for elements coughs and colds. However, its active principles, such as the digestive enzymes contained in the leaves, do not confirm this indication. The plant has been used to curdle milk, hence the name Butterwort.

flower stalk leafless

solitary flowers

leaves curled up around the edges

upper side of leaves sticky

flower stalk hairy

flower with a long spur (up to 25mm)

Bitter Milkwort

Polygala amara (milkwort family)
H 5–15cm   May–June   herbaceous perennial

basal leaves

2 large sepals
on either side
of flower

10–40 flowers
per raceme

In mediaeval herbals, Bitter Milkwort is recommended for increasing milk flow in cows, as is also reflected in the plant's scientific name (from Greek: *poly* = plenty and *gala* = milk). The plant was therefore not only used as a medicinal herb, but also added to animal fodder. In folk medicine, the plant was used to treat coughs, wounds and skin rashes and to aid digestion.

upper leaves

Habitat Rough grassland, fens and bogs, near springs. On alkaline soils. Central to south-eastern Europe, Britain.

> 3 fused petals, the lower one fringed
> short bracts alongside the flower stalk

petals fused

Rosemary

Rosmarinus officinalis (mint family)
H 50–200cm   Jan–Dec   shrub

Rosemary's essential oil is said to improve circulation, alleviate rheumatic and neuralgic pain, aid digestion, relieve flatulence and have antispasmodic properties. It is used as a tonic and mood-enhancer when feeling depressed, mentally tired or nervous. However, it should not be used as a herbal remedy when pregnant.

flower
10–12mm
long

leaves
needle-
shaped

Habitat Evergreen shrubland. Mediterranean. Commonly grown in gardens as ornamental shrub and medicinal or culinary herb.

> evergreen, aromatically scented shrub
> leaves curled down along the sides

2 protruding
stamens

Sage
Salvia officinalis (mint family)
H 20–70cm   May–July   shrub

Habitat *Originally from the Mediterranean, widely cultivated as a medicinal and culinary herb.*

> - releases an aromatic scent when bruised
> - low shrub, woody at base
> - green shoots covered in soft down

The scientific name *Salvia* is derived from the Latin word *salvare* = to heal. Greek and Roman physicians knew about the plant's diuretic, antispasmodic, carminative, haemostatic and antibacterial properties. It was used externally to stem bleeding and is known to reduce excessive sweating. Sage makes an excellent gargle for mouth and throat infections and Sage extract is added to toothpastes and mouthwashes. The essential oil contains thujone, which can be toxic in large quantities. Sage should be used with caution during pregnancy.

upper petal straight

calyx with 2-mm-long pointed tips

labiate flower up to 25mm long

152

leaves textured, finely toothed

4–8 flowers in whorls

Health tip
Sage tea against bloating and flatulence: use 1 tsp of the chopped leaves per cup (1–2 tsp per cup if using as a gargle), add boiling water, cover and leave to infuse for 10–15 minutes, then strain. Drink 3–4 cups per day.

Greek Sage
Salvia fruticosa (mint family)
H 30–150cm   March–June   shrub

The leaves of Greek Sage contain essential oils with slightly different components to those of the main species; in particular, it has a lower thujone content. The plant is a common household remedy in eastern Mediterranean countries, where it grows naturally in the wild. It is used as an antiseptic gargle for oral and throat infections and is taken as a tea.

Habitat Maquis, garigue. Greece, Crete, Cyprus, Turkey.

> leaves have a strong, aromatic scent
> green parts covered in hoary down
> leaves downy

labiate flower, 16–25mm long

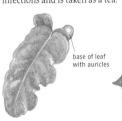

base of leaf with auricles

153

Clary Sage
Salvia sclarea (mint family)
H 30–120cm   May–Aug   biennial

Although it has no role in conventional medicine, Clary Sage has long been used in folk medicine to aid digestion and as a remedy for headaches, period pain, kidney complaints and colic. Applied externally, it aids the healing of infected wounds. The essential oil obtained from the flowering plant, also known as Muscatel oil.

stigma

anthers

Habitat Mediterranean, south-eastern Asia, cultivated as a medicinal and culinary herb in temperate regions of central and northern Europe.

> aromatic fragrance
> basal leaves heart-shaped, in a rosette
> flowers with large, purple bracts

labiate flower, up to 30mm long

leaves on stem irregularly ovate

Wild Pansy

Viola tricolor (violet family)

H 10–40cm   April–Sept   annual to herbaceous perennial

fruit capsule
in 3 sections

Habitat *Waysides, slopes, edges of fields, wasteland. Throughout most of Europe.*

> **flowers up to 3cm in size, in 3 colours**
> **only lower part of plant branching**

The Wild Pansy has a long history of use in folk medicine and is mentioned in numerous mediaeval herbals, where it is recommended for epilepsy, asthma and skin complaints. In modern herbal medicine, Wild Pansy is considered a depurative herb and is indicated for skin problems such as acne and eczema. In addition, it is used in the treatment of chest complaints such as bronchitis and whooping cough. The plant's alternative name, 'Heartsease', may be derived from its use in love charms, as mentioned in Shakespeare's Midsummer Night's Dream.

upper petals
blue-violet

leaves oval,
lobed or crenate

stipules
deeply
dissected

stripes on petals
lead insects towards
the nectar

flower
with spur

Health tip

To soothe a sore throat and ward off colds: use 2 tsp of Wild Pansy leaves and flowers per cup, add boiling water, infuse for 10 minutes, then strain. Drink several cups per day. You may also add some Lime blossom and honey to improve the flavour.

Sweet Violet
Viola odorata (violet family)
H 5–10cm   March–April   herbaceous perennial

The flowers of Sweet Violet contain essential oils, while the green parts and roots contain mucilage and alkaloids. Folk medicine uses them for their expectorant properties to treat coughs and other respiratory diseases. 'Syrup of Violets' was once a popular remedy and was taken as a cough syrup and a laxative. The flowers add colour to salads or, in dried form, to mixed herbal teas.

Habitat *Forest margins, waysides, hedgerows and gardens. Native to the Mediterranean and south-eastern Asia.*

> *solitary flowers on 3–7cm-long stalks*
> *all leaves basal*
> *forms runners*

petals
1–2cm long

heart-shaped
leaves

garden variety with
white flowers

spur
5–7mm long

x

155

Agnus Castus
Vitex agnus-castus (vervain family)
H 1–6m   June–Nov   shrub

leaves
palmate

The plant is also known as Chaste Tree or Monk's Pepper, as its fruits used to be chewed by mediaeval monks in a bid to curb sexual desire. An extract from the fruit is used in modern herbal medicine for premenstrual tension, painful or irregular periods, and to relieve the symptoms of the menopause. The leaves were used as a folk remedy against fever.

Habitat *Along riverbanks, on damp ground. Mediterranean to northern India.*

> *deciduous*
> *flowers blue, violet or pink*
> *berries purplish-black, 5mm in diameter*

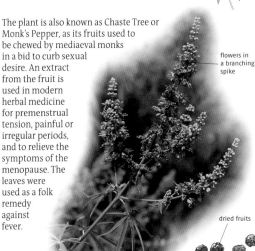

flowers in
a branching
spike

petals
6–9mm long

dried fruits

Black Mustard
Brassica nigra (mustard family)
H 50–100cm   June–Sept   annual

Habitat *Fields, wasteland sites, rubble, along waysides. Prefers wet ground. Native to southern and western Europe, naturalised worldwide.*

> **4 sepals, stiffly upright, spread out**
> **leaves stalked, lower leaves deeply lobed, with a large terminal lobe**

The seeds, which are really dark brown, rather than black, are the key ingredient in mustard. The plant has antibacterial properties and stimulates the circulatory and digestive systems. Mustard plasters have traditionally been used to treat rheumatic and neuralgic pain. However, if left on for too long, mustard plasters can cause serious skin irritation.

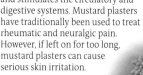

flowers 5–9mm across

seed pods angular or flattened, tight against the stem

all leaves stalked

Wild Cabbage
Brassica oleracea var. *oleracea* (mustard family)
H 30–250cm   May–Sept   biennial

Habitat *Western Mediterranean, sea cliffs and coastal areas in Britain and northern Europe.*

> **Wild form of vegetable cabbage**
> **a cabbage is the much enlarged bud of the plant**

Wild Cabbage and its varieties are probably one of the oldest known vegetables in the world. It is mentioned in Greek mythology, where cabbage is claimed to have sprung from the sweat of Zeus. Fresh cabbage juice is recommended as a cure for gastro-intestinal ulcers. Poultices of cabbage leaves were placed on wounds and sores. Sauerkraut helps against constipation.

petals 1–2cm long

stem smooth, glabrous

section through a cabbage

Greater Celandine

Chelidonium majus var. *majus* (poppy family)

H 30–70cm   April–Oct   herbaceous perennial   ☠

The herb contains a number of alkaloids and therefore counts as a mildly poisonous plant. Pliny observed that swallows (chelidon in Greek) used the milky sap from the plant to help open the eyes of their young. In folk medicine, the sap was used to treat warts and corns. Conventional medicine uses substances from this plant in medications for liver and gall bladder complaints.

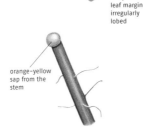

leaf margin irregularly lobed

Health tip

Due to the plant's toxicity, it should only be used in consultation with a qualified herbal practitioner. For external application, prepare an infusion with 2 tsp of the herb. Leave for 10 minutes and apply as a wrap.

orange-yellow sap from the stem

Habitat *Waysides, in hedgerows, forest margins, common weed in gardens. On loamy, nutrient-rich soils. Throughout Europe and Asia.*

> *Leaves pinnate, leaflets oval, crenate*
> *seeds in long, thin pods*
> *2 pale yellow sepals*

4 petals, 5–10mm long

 157

profusion of stamens

Wallflower

Erysimum cheiri (mustard family)

H 20–80cm   May–June   herbaceous perennial

The plant's name is probably derived from its preference for growing on old walls and in other dry, rubbly habitats. According to Hippocrates, the herb was used in ancient Greece to treat uterine infections. In folk medicine, the flowers were used as a depurative, a laxative, a remedy for liver and heart conditions and to regulate the monthly cycle. These days it is mainly used in homeopathy.

flower up to 5cm in diameter

leaves alternate

leaves narrow, hairy

Californian Poppy

Eschscholzia californica (poppy family)

H 30–50cm   June–Oct   annual to biennial

Although introduced to Europe only quite recently as an ornamental plant, the Californian Poppy has found applications in both folk medicine and homeopathy. It is taken for pain relief, for colics and abdominal cramps, nervous tension and insomnia. In conventional medicine, extracts from the plant are used, in combination with other ingredients, for the same indications.

leaves feathery

flower 3–4cm across

Lady's Bedstraw

Galium verum (bedstraw family)
H 30–60cm   June–Sept   herbaceous perennial

The flowering herb contains a protein that acts as a curdling agent and the plant has therefore been employed in cheesemaking. As a side effect it gave the cheese a rich yellow colour. The dried plant is strongly scented and was used as a strewing herb.
A variety of applications for Lady's Bedstraw are known in folk medicine: it is used as a diuretic and a remedy for catarrhs, in Ireland it was placed on burns and skin disorders and in France it was used in the treatment of epilepsy.

leaves needle-shaped, in whorls

individual flowers star-shaped

Habitat Meadows and pastures, fens and wetlands, waysides. On alkaline soils. Europe, western Asia, North America.

> *flowers in a branching, upright panicle*
> *flowers are honey-scented*
> *stem angular, 4-sided*

flower 2–3mm across

159

Health tip

A soothing bath to ease aching legs: place 50 grams of Lady's Bedstraw into 1 litre of water and bring to the boil. Simmer for 5 minutes, then strain and add to your bath or footbath.

Witch Hazel
Hamamelis virginiana (witch-hazel family)
H 2–8m   Oct–Feb   shrub

Habitat *Deciduous forests of North America, introduced to Europe as an ornamental shrub.*

> deciduous
> flowers appear around the same time as fruits from the previous year ripen

petals narrow, ribbon-like

sepals downy

North American Indians used the bark of this shrub to treat wounds, eye problems, diarrhoea, oral and throat infections and period pain. Witch Hazel is known in Europe mainly as an ornamental, winter-flowering shrub in parks and gardens. The leaves and bark contain tannins, and Witch Hazel extract is a common ingredient in eye drops, creams, ointments and skin tonics.

leaves look similar to hazel leaves

bark contains tannins

160

Bay Tree
Laurus nobilis (laurel family)
H 2–20m   March–April   tree or shrub

Habitat *Forests in the Mediterranean, in northern Europe as an ornamental garden plant.*

> evergreen
> male and female flowers on separate plants

flowers yellow to white

In Greek mythology, Bay – or Laurel – is sacred to Apollo and his son Asclepius, the gods of healing and medicine. It was held in high esteem as a medicinal plant throughout the Middle Ages and beyond. Nowadays, Bay leaves are mostly known as an aromatic flavouring in soups and stews. In folk medicine, Bay was used to treat stomach complaints and to ease rheumatic pain.

fruits fleshy, oval

leaves stiff, leathery, lanceolate

leaf margins wavy

flowers in clusters

Evening Primrose

Oenothera biennis (evening-primrose family)

H 50–200cm   June–Aug   biennial

The seeds of Evening Primrose contain a valuable oil with up to 14% gamma-linolenic acid, an essential fatty acid, which is used in the treatment of eczema and other skin complaints. It is also thought to help lower cholesterol levels. Evening Primrose supplements are a popular herbal remedy taken to ease premenstrual tension. The leaves have been used as a remedy for diarrhoea.

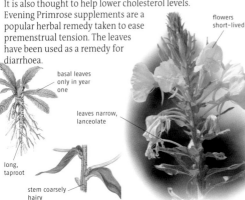

Habitat *Originally from North America, naturalised in Europe on rubble, wasteland and along railway embankments.*

> **basal rosette only in year one**
> **flowers open in the evening**

flowers short-lived

basal leaves only in year one

leaves narrow, lanceolate

long, taproot

stem coarsely hairy

petals up to 5cm long

161

Tormentil

Potentilla erecta (rose family)

H 10–30cm   May–Aug   herbaceous perennial

The root of this plant is particularly rich in tannins, and Tormentil has a long history as a medicinal herb in conventional and folk medicine as well as in homeopathy. It has strongly astringent and haemostatic properties, both in external and internal application. It is also used as a remedy for diarrhoea.

Habitat *Heaths and moors, rough grassland, blanket bogs, open woodland. Northern and central Europe, northern Asia.*

> **stem prostrate or decumbent**
> **leaves trifoliate, but with 2 large stipules**

root deep red and woody

flowers 1cm across

Common Buckthorn

Rhamnus cathartica (buckthorn family)

H 1–3m   May–June   shrub   ☠

Habitat Hedgerows, forest margins. Usually on alkaline soils. Europe, northern Africa, Asia.

> **flowers in dense clusters in the leaf axils**
> **usually 4, sometimes 5 petals**
> **leaves opposite**

The earliest descriptions of buckthorn as a medicinal plant go back to ancient Greece, and the plant is also mentioned in Anglo-Saxons records dating from before the Norman conquest. In folklore it was believed to offer protection from demons and witches. The berries act as a strong laxative and have therefore been used as a remedy for constipation.

In folk medicine, a tea made from buckthorn berries was recommended as a depurative. A homeopathic remedy from the fruits is prescribed for gastro-intestinal complaints.

pea-sized berries

flowers greenish-yellow

secondary shoots

branches often terminating in a spiny thorn

162

Health tip

Buckthorn tea as a laxative (use with caution – only take in consultation with a qualified herbal practitioner!): use 1/2 tsp of chopped berries per cup, add boiling water. Infuse for 10–15 minutes and strain. Drink no more than 1 cup per day.

leaves shiny, tough and leathery

flower star-shaped with black and white stamens

Rue
Ruta graveolens (rue family)
H 30–50cm   June–Aug   herbaceous perennial   ☠

Rue has been used as a medicinal plant since antiquity, where it is said to have been an ingredient in King Mithridates' legendary antidote to all poisons. Emperor Charlemagne recommended its cultivation in his provinces. It is used as a remedy for colics and period pain, liver and gall bladder complaints and for oral and throat infections. The oil has been used to induce abortion and the plant should therefore not be used during pregnancy. The sap can cause blistering or dermatitis in some people.

Habitat Native to the eastern Mediterranean, naturalised on walls, waste ground and rubble.

> leaves blueish-green
> aromatic fragrance
> flowers in umbels
>   – terminal flower with 5 petals, others with 4

Health tip

For a soothing herbal drink, mix Rue, Valerian, Lemon Balm and Hawthorn flowers to equal parts (using Rue on its own is not recommended). Use 1 heaped tsp of the mix per cup, add warm water, cover and leave to infuse for 10 hours.

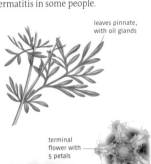

leaves pinnate, with oil glands

terminal flower with 5 petals

flower up to 2cm in diameter

flower with 4 petals

163

White Mustard
Sinapis alba (mustard family)
H 30–60cm   June–Sept   annual

Habitat Fields and waste ground. Native to the Mediterranean, naturalised from cultivation.

> seed pods hairy, with long glabrous beak
> sepals spread out

The pale-coloured seeds of White Mustard are used in mild mustards. The plant has been cultivated in northern Europe since the 9th century. Mustard plasters or poultices are used to improve circulation and are a common household remedy for respiratory infections, arthritic joints, chilblains and skin conditions. In Bach flower remedies, mustard is used to lift depression.

petals 7–10mm long

leaves irregularly toothed

mustard is made from the powdered seeds

164

Hedge Mustard
Sisymbrium officinale (mustard family)
H 30–60cm   May–Oct   annual

Habitat Road verges, disturbed ground, wasteland and rubble. Europe, Asia.

> widespread colonising weed
> lower leaves deeply lobed
> flowers in stiffly branching spikes

The young shoots of this inconspicuous plant contain cardiac glycosides, which in larger doses can be poisonous. In folk medicine, the herb has been used to treat throat infections, hoarseness and bronchitis as well as gall bladder complaints. A homeopathic preparation of Hedge Mustard is indicated for laryngitis.

seed pods 8–20mm long

seed pods aligned alongside the stem

seed pods ripen as flowering continues at top of flower spike

flowers up to 7mm across

Agrimony

Agrimonia eupatoria (rose family)

H 30–100cm   June–Sept   herbaceous perennial

The name Agrimony is derived from the Greek word argemone, referring to plants that were considered beneficial for the eyes, while the scientific name *eupatoria* refers to Mithridates Eupator, an ancient Greek king renowned for his herbal skills, in particular his famous antidote to all poisons. In modern herbalism it is mainly used for its tannins and is prescribed for mild diarrhoea, as a gargle for oral and throat infections, externally, for skin conditions and as a remedy for bed-wetting.

Habitat Hedgerows, forests, shrubland, rough grassland. Europe, south-western Asia, northern Africa.

> **lower leaves in a rosette**
> **stem and leaves downy**

fruit with hooked bracts

petals 4–6mm long

165

flowers in a tall raceme

leaves irregularly pinnate

Health tip

Agrimony gargle for the treatment of sore throats and oral infections: use 1/2 tsp of the flowering herb per cup. Add boiling water and infuse for 10–15 minutes. Strain and use fresh, 2–4 times daily.

Dill

Anethum graveolens (parsley family)

H 40–120cm   July–Aug   annual

Habitat *Originally from the Mediterranean and south-western Asia, cultivated worldwide as a culinary herb.*

> aromatic fragrance
> leaves soft and feathery, with needle-shaped leaflets

Dill is best known as a culinary herb used in fish dishes and fresh salads. The herb itself is said to act as a stomachic; the seeds are used to aid digestion and for their antispasmodic and carminative properties. The Egyptian Ebers Papyrus (1550 BC) recommends Dill as a cure for headaches. In homeopathy it is prescribed for high blood pressure.

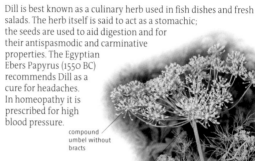

compound umbel without bracts

ribbed seeds

umbel with 20–50 rays

very fine, feathery leaves

individual flower 2–3mm in diameter

Garden Angelica

Angelica archangelica (parsley family)

H 120–250cm   June–Aug   herbaceous perennial

Habitat *Native to northern and eastern Europe, western Asia, naturalised in central Europe in moist and shady places, along rivers and ditches.*

> flowers in large globular umbels
> large, parchment-like sheath at leaf base
> stem at base up to 10cm strong

Sixteenth century herbals recommend Garden Angelica root soaked in vinegar as protection against evil spirits and witchcraft – and also against the plague. Today, the root is used to combat loss of appetite, digestive complaints and flatulence. An essential oil from the seeds is used as a rub for rheumatic pain.

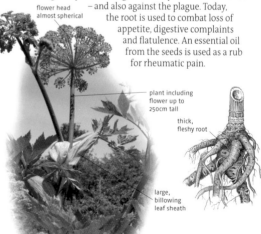

flower head almost spherical

plant including flower up to 250cm tall

thick, fleshy root

large, billowing leaf sheath

compound umbel consisting of 20–40 smaller umbels

Colocynth

Citrullus colocynthis (gourd family)
H 30–50cm   June–Aug   herbaceous perennial

The dried fruits of the Colocynth (also known as 'Bitter Apple' or 'Bitter Cucumber'), have long been known as an effective laxative. However, they also contain toxins, which can cause very strong reactions in the gut and are therefore no longer used in herbal medicine. Extracts from the fruits were used in the past as an insect repellent, in particular against moths and bedbugs.

fruits up to 12cm in size

leaves with 3–5 deeply dissected lobes

Habitat Native to the southern Mediterranean, south-western Asia and India.

> creeping stems, covered in coarse hairs
> thrives even in very sandy soils

flower 10–15mm in diameter

Rock Samphire

Crithmum maritimum (parsley family)
H 40–60cm   June–Aug   herbaceous perennial

Although no longer used as a medicinal plant, Rock Samphire has played an important role in the past for its diuretic and carminative properties. The 16th century herbalist John Gerard recommends the leaves as 'wholesome for the stoppings of the liver, milt and kidnies'. For its high vitamin C content, the plant was taken by sailors to prevent scurvy.

Habitat Rocky shorelines, Atlantic coast from Scotland to Portugal, Mediterranean and Black Sea.

> plant looks fleshy
> leaves bright green

small flowers in umbels

leaves deeply dissected

individual flowers tiny

ovary ribbed

Pumpkin
Cucurbita pepo (gourd family)
H creeping, up to 10m long   June–Oct   annual

Pliny mentions the Pumpkin in his writings, although it seems unlikely that he was referring to this North American species of the plant. Pumpkin seeds contain amino acids, trace elements (selenium, zinc, manganese), vitamin E and other substances (e.g. phytosterols). In the past, large quantities of the seeds were taken to expel tapeworms and other intestinal parasites. Nowadays, Pumpkin seed preparations are prescribed for benign prostate enlargement and complaints of the urinary tract.

seeds
flat-oval

different types of pumpkins

flower up to 10cm across

leaves heart-shaped

flowers on long stalks

168

flower trumpet-shaped

Health tip
To complement the therapy of benign prostate enlargement, take 1–2 tbsp of pumpkin seeds twice a day, for example, with cereals or yoghurt.

Squirting Cucumber

Ecballium elaterium (gourd family)
H 20–100cm   April–Oct   herbaceous perennial   ☠

Hippocrates recommends this plant as a laxative, but also warns of its side effects, which include inflammation, stomach pain and vomiting. Nevertheless, the juice from its roots or fruits was used for this purpose for a long time. Modern medical research has found substances in this plant that appear to inhibit the growth of cancer cells.

Habitat Wasteland, along waysides. Mediterranean region and southern Europe.

> *entire plant covered in stiff hairs*
> *fruits explode on contact, ejecting the seeds with a mucilaginous liquid*
> *male and female flowers on the same plant*

fruit deflexed

fruit spiky

flower 4–5cm across

Fennel

Foeniculum vulgare (parsley family)
H 50–200cm   July–Oct   annual to perennial

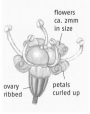

Fennel seeds contain essential oils and are taken as an expectorant in the treatment of coughs and colds as well as for their soothing effect on the digestive system. Fennel tea has long been used as a safe and effective remedy for flatulence, especially in infants. In folk medicine it was used to stimulate milk flow in nursing mothers.

Habitat Wild form originates from the Mediterranean, worldwide in cultivation.

> *fine, feathery leaves*
> *flowers in a flat umbel*

compound umbel with 15–25 rays

umbels without bracts

fine, feathery leaves

fruit in sections

seeds with 5 ridges

flowers ca. 2mm in size

ovary ribbed

petals curled up

Wood Avens
Geum urbanum (rose family)
H 30–120cm   May–Oct   herbaceous perennial

Habitat *Forests, along fences, waysides, waste ground. Europe to western Asia.*

> **indicates nutrient-rich soil**
> **stem softly hairy**
> **green sepals alternate with petals of the same length**

flowers
1–2cm in diameter

In mediaeval times, Wood Avens was held in high regard as a medicinal plant and was known as 'the Blessed Herb', *Herba benedicta*. Its alternative name, 'Herb Bennet' is derived from this. In fact, apart from tannins and essential oils, the root contains few active elements. The herb is still used in folk medicine for its tannins, and is recommended against loss of appetite, digestive disorders and diarrhoea, oral and throat infections and, externally, as a treatment for rashes and eczema.

leaves on stem trifoliate

stipules

fruit with hooked styles

Health tip
Wood Avens tea for digestive complaints or as a gargle: use 1 tsp per cup, add boiling water and infuse for 15 minutes. Strain and drink before meals. To be taken in moderation.

Rupturewort

Herniaria glabra (pink family)
H 5–30cm June–Oct annual or perennial

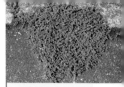

As both the English and the scientific names suggest, this herb was used in former times as a cure for hernia. The green parts of the plant contain tannins, saponins and flavonoids. The herb has antispasmodic properties and is indicated for bladder and kidney complaints. Folk medicine recommends it as a depurative.

Habitat Dunes, waysides, dry grassland, railway embankments. Central Europe, northern Africa, western Asia.

> drought-tolerant, indicates sandy soil
> stems prostrate
> flowers in clusters in the leaf axils

petals
yellowish–green

leaves
3–8mm long

7–10 flowers
per cluster

Lovage

Levisticum officinale (parsley family)
H 1–2m July–Aug herbaceous perennial

individual
leaflet, used as
a kitchen herb

In continental Europe, the aromatic leaves of this plant are a common flavouring in soups and stews. Mediaeval herbalists recommended the root for a variety of ailments, but its use later went out of fashion. It is said to have diuretic, digestive, expectorant and anti-inflammatory properties and was used for infections of the urinary tract, colds and catarrhs and to regulate the menstrual cycle. Do not use when pregnant.

Habitat Native to south-western Asia. In Europe occasionally naturalised.

> plant has a spicy, savoury fragrance
> round stem, ribbed, hollow
> leaves bi- or tri-pinnate

compound
umbel with
bracts

thick,
branching root

umbel with
8–20 rays

St John's Wort
Hypericum perforatum (St John's wort family)
H 30–60cm July–Aug herbaceous perennial

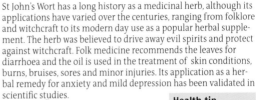

Habitat Heath and rough grassland, wasteland and rubble. Europe, Asia.

> stem with 2 vertical ribs
> flowers release a red liquid when bruised
> grown commercially for its oil

St John's Wort has a long history as a medicinal herb, although its applications have varied over the centuries, ranging from folklore and witchcraft to its modern day use as a popular herbal supplement. The herb was believed to drive away evil spirits and protect against witchcraft. Folk medicine recommends the leaves for diarrhoea and the oil is used in the treatment of skin conditions, burns, bruises, sores and minor injuries. Its application as a herbal remedy for anxiety and mild depression has been validated in scientific studies.

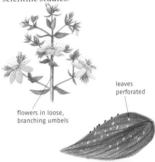

petals not quite symmetrical

flowers in loose, branching umbels

leaves perforated

Health tip
St John's Wort oil for sunburn and minor burns: crush ca. 25g of fresh St John's Wort flowers and place in a clear bottle together with 1/2 litre of oil. Leave to infuse in the uncorked bottle for 3–5 days, then cork the bottle and leave in a sunny place for 5–6 weeks until the oil has turned red.

stamens in 3 groups

Creeping Jenny
Lysimachia nummularia (primrose family)
H 10–50cm   May–July   herbaceous perennial

The plant's scientific name refers to Lysimachos, a Macedonian officer who served under Alexander the Great. It was held in high regard in mediaeval times and was thought to be a remedy for up to 100 illnesses. It is still used in folk medicine to treat coughs, diarrhoea, rheumatic complaints, eczema and grazes or cuts.

Habitat Wetland meadows, lowland forests, near water, in ditches, along waysides. On damp soils. Throughout most of Europe.

> creeping stems
> leaves wintergreen
> tips of sepals with red marks

leaves round, 3cm in size

flowers on long stalks

flowers 1–2.5cm across

Yellow Loosestrife
Lysimachia vulgaris (primrose family)
H 50–150cm   June–Aug   herbaceous perennial

Yellow Loosestrife never enjoyed quite the same acclaim as its cousin of the *Lysimachia* genus, the Creeping Jenny. Nevertheless, it was a popular wound herb, and Dioscorides recommends burning it as incense to drive away snakes and flies. In folk medicine it was used for its tannins as a remedy for diarrhoea and was taken to prevent scurvy.

Habitat Fens, ditches, near springs, lowland forests. On wet ground. Throughout most of Europe, Asia, northern Africa.

> stem upright, hairy
> terminal flowers in upper leaf axils
> tips of sepals with a reddish tinge

flowers 1.5–2.5cm across

2–4 leaves around the nodes

Wild Parsnip
Pastinaca sativa (parsley family)
H 30–100cm   July–Sept   biennial

Habitat *Meadows, waysides, on disturbed ground, wasteland. Mostly on alkaline soils. Western Asia, Europe.*

> *prefers loamy soils*
> *wild form of the root vegetable*
> *leaves odd-pinnate*

Parsnips are primarily known as a popular winter vegetable. However, the plant also has healing powers. Parsnip root was used in folk medicine to treat toothache, stomach, kidney and lung complaints and to aid digestion. The seeds were used as a spice and were thought to be a remedy for bladder problems.

umbel with 7–20 rays

carrot-shaped root

individual flowers 2mm across

Parsley

flat-leaved Parsley

Petroselinum crispum (parsley family)
H 30–100cm   April–Aug   biennial

Habitat *Only known in cultivation, presumed to originate from south-western Asia and the Mediterranean.*

> *numerous sub-species and varieties for culinary use*
> *leaves bi- or tri-pinnate, leaflets triangular*

The ancient Greeks knew Parsley almost exclusively as a medicinal plant, whereas the Romans also used it as a culinary herb – and as a symbolic plant in funeral ceremonies. The seeds stimulate the digestive and urinary tracts and were used to induce abortion. The root and leaves contain less essential oil than the seeds. Parsley seeds should not be used when pregnant or if suffering from kidney infection.

individual flowers are tiny

umbel with 10–20 rays

curly Parsley

Silverweed

Potentilla anserina (rose family)

H 15–80cm   May–Aug   herbaceous perennial

The dried herb is rich in tannins and is typically prescribed for diarrhoea and to relieve oral or throat infections. It is used as an antispasmodic remedy for period pain and cramps. In wraps and poultices it is said to help with slow-healing wounds. In homeopathy, *Potentilla* is indicated for gastro-intestinal complaints.

Habitat Waysides and road verges, fields, wasteland. Throughout the northern hemisphere.

> indicates nutrient-poor, compacted soil
> runners up to 1m long

leaves pinnate, leaflets serrate

rooting at nodes

creeping stems

flowers up to 3cm across

solitary flowers on long stalks

175

Health tip

Silverweed gargle or mouthwash for gum problems and sore throats: use 1–2 tsp of the dried herb per cup. Add hot water and infuse for 10 minutes. Strain and use lukewarm, several times per day. For stomach cramps and colics, add Lemon Balm and Peppermint and drink while still hot as a tea.

Cowslip
Primula veris ssp. *veris* (primrose family)
H 10–30cm   March–June   herbaceous perennial

Habitat *Rough grassland, meadows, forest margins, open woodland. Usually on alkaline soils. Throughout most of Europe, Asia.*

> scented flowers on a leafless stalk
> all flowers facing to one side

As a plant that flowers in early spring, the Cowslip had a special place in Norse mythology. It was dedicated to the goddess Freya and was believed to be protected by magical creatures. The roots have diuretic properties and are used as a remedy for catarrhs of the respiratory system. Cowslip tea is taken to calm the nerves.

calyx 10–15mm long

red dots at base of petals

leaves up to 12cm long, 'wrinkly'

calyx pouched

Buttercup
Ranunculus acris (buttercup family)
H 30–100cm   May–Sept   herbaceous perennial

Habitat *Meadows, pastures. On damp soils. Widespread in Europe and Asia.*

> dominant feature on damp meadows in May
> indicates nutrient-rich soil
> flowers golden-yellow, shiny inside

Many a gardener would happily do without this medicinal plant, which has a habit of spreading through lawns. Although the fresh herb can irritate the skin, it has been used in poultices for chronic skin conditions as well as for rheumatic complaints and gout. It was also known as a household remedy for constipation and intestinal worms. In modern herbal medicine its use has become obsolete.

basal leaves with 5–7 lobes

flowers 2–3cm across

Madder

Rubia tinctorum (bedstraw family)

H 50–100cm   June–Aug   herbaceous perennial

Powdered Madder root has been used as a red dye since Roman times. Until the advent of chemical dyes, the red trousers of French soldiers were dyed using Madder. Madder tea is said to help prevent bladder and kidney stones, cure infections and relieve cramps. In folk medicine the plant is known as a remedy for diarrhoea.

Habitat *Dry, rocky, open ground. Mediterranean region, south-eastern Europe, western Asia.*

> **stem angular, prickly**
> **flowers in branching panicles**

dye is produced from the powdered root

leaves in whorls

individual flowers just 2–3mm across

177

Common Stonecrop

Sedum acre (stonecrop family)

H 5–15cm   June–Aug   herbaceous perennial ☠

Common Stonecrop was once an established remedy for heart disease, circulatory disorders, high blood pressure and fevers; externally it was used as a wound herb and to treat warts, corns and psoriasis. Culpeper recommends it for scurvy, though he is otherwise critical of it. Excessive doses of the fleshy leaves can cause vomiting and diarrhoea, and the sap may cause blistering and skin irritation.

Habitat *Rocky and stony ground, on walls, in the cracks of pavements, on gravel. Warm and sunny places in well-drained soil. Europe, western Asia.*

> **colonising plant**
> **leaves fleshy, underside rounded, flat on top**

flower 15–20mm across

leaves in 4 vertical rows

petals with pointed tips

Small-leaved Lime
Tilia cordata (lime family)
H up to 25m   June–July   tree

Habitat *Deciduous forests, parks, village greens, along roads. Europe, as far as the Ural Mountains.*

> **Large-leaved Lime has the same medicinal properties**
> **4–12 flowers in a cluster**
> **leaves unevenly heart-shaped**

long linear bract

flowers in clusters of 4–12

Both the Small-leaved and Large-leaved Lime have the same active components and are used for the same indications. Lime (or Linden) blossom tea has been known for its diaphoretic properties since mediaeval times. Modern medical research, however, is uncertain whether this is really due to the lime flowers or merely an effect of drinking the hot liquid. What is certain is that they contain throat-soothing mucilage, while lime blossom tea may also stimulate the immune system.

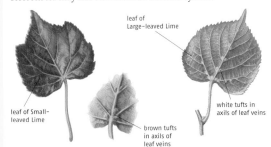

leaf of Large-leaved Lime

leaf of Small-leaved Lime

brown tufts in axils of leaf veins

white tufts in axils of leaf veins

Health tip

Lime blossom tea to calm the nerves and ward off colds: use 1 tsp of dried lime flowers per cup, add boiling water and infuse for 10–15 minutes. Strain and drink hot, sweetened with honey. Alternatively, try adding rosehips, Camomile, Mallow or Meadowsweet flowers to the lime blossom.

bract

fruits of the Small-leaved Lime

Puncture Vine

Tribulus terrestris (caltrop family)

H 10–60cm   May–Sept   annual

Both of the plant's English names (the other being Goathead) refer to its fruits, which have long, hard spikes. An extract from the herb has been used in Ayurvedic medicine for centuries and is also known as a folk remedy in Mediterranean countries. More recently, it has been marketed successfully as a herbal supplement said to raise testosterone levels and thereby increase muscle tissue and improve sex drive.

leaflets lanceolate

solitary flowers

creeping stem

flowers 4–5mm across

Mullein

Verbascum densiflorum (figwort family)

H 50–250cm   July–Sept   biennial

Before the introduction of cotton, this downy plant served to make lamp wicks and torches, as is reflected in some of its older names, such as 'Candlewick Plant' or 'Torches'. Apparently this use goes back to the Romans, who knew the plant under the name of Candela regia. However, the flowers are also rich in mucilage and were taken as a tea to relieve colds and coughs, as a diuretic and to ease rheumatic pain.

flowers in a tall spike

leaves decurrent

flower 30–35mm across

Pheasant's Eye

Adonis vernalis (buttercup family)

H 10–40cm   April–May   herbaceous perennial

Habitat Rough grass-
land, sunny slopes
on chalk. Native to
south-eastern Europe,
western Asia.

> solitary, terminal flowers
  with 5 green sepals
> flowers open only in full
  sunshine

The plant contains cardiac glycosides and should not be used
for self-medication. Modern medicine prescribes it for heart
conditions and low blood pressure. In folk medicine, the herb
has long been known as a remedy for oedema,
fevers and period pain. In homeopathy it is
used to treat angina.

10–20 shiny petals

flower 4–6cm across

leaflets narrow
and feathery,
just 1mm wide

leaves feathery

180

Century Plant

Agave americana (agave family)

H 300–800cm   June–Aug   herbaceous perennial

Habitat Native to
Mexico. Cultivated
as an ornamental
plant and naturalised
in Mediterranean
countries.

> flowers in year ten
> large fleshy leaves in a
  basal rosette
> leaves pointed, up to 2m
  long, with spiny edges

The Mayas and Aztecs used the fresh juice from this plant as a
vulnerary and a remedy for diarrhoea. It also forms the basis
for alcoholic drinks, such as tequila.
In Mediterranean folk medicine the
Agave is largely ignored. However, it is
used in homeopathy in the treatment
of sore gums
and anaemia.

leaves up
to 2m long

flowers
7–9cm long

Aloe Vera

Aloe vera (aloe family)

H 50–100cm   Jan–Dec   herbaceous perennial

Aloe-based products have become a familiar feature in cosmetics and natural healthcare. The fresh sap from its leaves does indeed have proven medicinal properties. It promotes healing in minor injuries, insect bites and sunburn, has antibacterial properties and, taken internally, the gel acts as a laxative and pain relief as well as boosting the immune system. Nevertheless, its effectiveness as a dietary supplement is disputed. The use of Aloe Vera gel during pregnancy is not recommended.

Habitat Native to northern Africa and Arabic countries, cultivated in the Mediterranean. In central and northern Europe mainly grown in pots and planters.

> **leaves in a basal rosette, fleshy and pointed, with spiny edges**
> **flowers in a dense raceme, up to 120cm tall**

flowers reddish-yellow

individual flowers on stalks

flowers tubular, up to 3cm long

   181

leaves up to 60cm long

leaf sap gel-like

Health tip

Aloe Vera is often sold as a pot plant for the garden or windowsill. The plant is handy as a quick remedy for insect bites. Simply cut off a leaf from your plant and place it cut side down on the affected area.

Arnica
Arnica montana (daisy family)
H 20–50cm   June–July   herbaceous perennial

Habitat *Grassland, pastures, heaths, moors, on acidic soils. In mountainous areas throughout Europe.*

> large leaves in a basal rosette
> flower stem with 2–3 pairs of small, opposite leaves
> capitulum with disc and ray florets

Although unknown in antiquity, Arnica has been a popular medicinal plant since the 17th century. The philosopher and poet Johann Wolfgang von Goethe swore by it and used to take Arnica to ease his angina in old age. In fact, Arnica is now considered poisonous and internal use is no longer recommended. A cream or tincture from the dried flowers, applied externally, may be used to treat bruises and sprains, rheumatic pain and aching joints. It should be used with caution though, as some people develop allergic skin reactions to the plant.

capitulum
4–8cm across

branching root

small, opposite leaves on stem

Health tip

Arnica is not found outside gardens in the UK. For an Arnica gargle, use 1 tsp of dried flowers per cup, add boiling water and infuse for 10 minutes, then strain. Use lukewarm as a gargle. Do not swallow!

1–3 flower heads per plant

ray florets 3–6mm across

Southernwood
Artemisia abrotanum (daisy family)
H 50–120cm   July–Oct   herbaceous perennial

In England, judges used to place bunches of Southernwood and Rue at the side of the prisoner in the dock to protect themselves against 'jail fever' – typhus infections brought into court from the overcrowded prisons. In folk medicine, the plant was used as a digestive tonic, as a remedy for period pain and to expel intestinal parasites. Its use has now become obsolete.

Habitat Native to southern and eastern Europe, western Asia. In northern Europe cultivated as a medicinal plant.

> dwarf shrub
> strong citrus scent
> capitulum with disc florets only

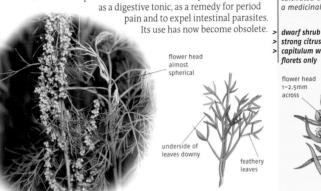

flower head almost spherical

underside of leaves downy

feathery leaves

flower head 1–2.5mm across

183

Common Wormwood
Artemisia absinthium (daisy family)
H 60–120cm   July–Sept   herbaceous perennial ☠

Wormwood tastes extremely bitter but also contains essential oils. As the scientific species name indicates, it was once a key ingredient in absinthe. However, its high thujone content led to hallucinations and nowadays only the bitter agents are extracted for this purpose. Used medicinally, the herb is said to stimulate the appetite, aid digestion and relieve colic. The essential oil is no longer in use as it is considered toxic and potentially carcinogenic.

Habitat Waysides, on walls, wasteland and rubble. On nutrient-rich soils. Europe and Asia.

> base of plant woody
> aromatic fragrance
> entire plant covered in hoary down

leaves on stem deeply dissected

nodding, spherical flower heads

capitulum 2–4mm across

Tarragon
Artemisia dracunculus (daisy family)
H 60–120cm   Aug–Oct   herbaceous perennial

Habitat *Native to eastern Russia and Mongolia, cultivated worldwide as a culinary herb.*

> **plant glabrous, aromatically scented**
> **numerous small flower heads in branching spikes**

capitulum just 2mm across

In mediaeval times, Tarragon was thought to be an antidote to snake poison, though this probably belongs in the realm of myth. The herb contains essential oils and a number of other active components. It is primarily used as a kitchen herb, especially in French cuisine, and as a flavouring in herb vinegars. In folk medicine, it is used to stimulate the appetite and for its diuretic and digestive properties.

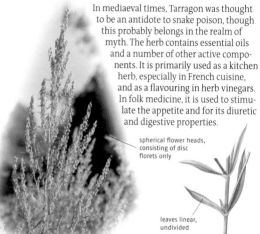

spherical flower heads, consisting of disc florets only

leaves linear, undivided

Mugwort
Artemisia vulgaris (daisy family)
H 60–250cm   July–Nov   herbaceous perennial

Habitat *Waysides, rubble and wasteland, near water. Widespread throughout Europe and Asia.*

> **numerous small flower heads**
> **disc florets only, yellow to red**
> **subtly fragrant when bruised**

capitulum 3–4mm long

Mugwort has a long and varied history as a medicinal plant. Apparently, Roman soldiers used to line their sandals with the herb to prevent blisters and tired feet, while the Welsh Physicians of Myddfai suggested that 'if a woman be unable to give birth to her child let the Mugwort be bound to her left thigh'. In addition, the herb was used to expel intestinal worms, to stimulate the appetite, aid digestion and as a culinary herb.

capitulum oval

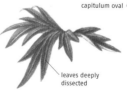

leaves deeply dissected

Common Barberry

Berberis vulgaris (barberry family)
H up to 300cm   April–June   shrub ☠

oblong berries,
up to 1cm long

The refreshingly tart fruits of this shrub are rich in vitamin C and can be used in jams and compotes. Folk medicine uses them as a laxative and for liver and spleen problems. The poisonous bark of the root, too, was used in the past as a remedy for gall bladder complaints, jaundice, digestive disorders, diarrhoea, kidney stones, rheumatism and numerous other ailments.

Habitat Forest margins, hedgerows, open pine forests. Europe to western Asia.

> deciduous
> leaves in bunches
> flowers have an intense, slightly unpleasant fragrance

flowers in
pendent
racemes

long, very sharp
spines, often in
threes

6 sepals
and 6 petals

185

Trifid Bur-marigold

Bidens tripartita (daisy family)
H 15–100cm   July–Oct   annual

In the past, this plant was valued as a remedy for bladder and kidney stones, fevers, haemorrhoids, ruptured blood-vessels and bleeding of any kind. Culpeper praises it highly, saying it 'cutteth and cleanseth thick and tough humours of the breast, it opens obstructions of the liver, mollifies hardness of the spleen and strengthens the lungs exceedingly'.

Habitat Near water, in ditches, wasteland, wet meadows. On damp, nutrient-rich soils. Common throughout Europe and Britain.

> colonising plant on muddy ground
> capitulum with disc florets only
> leaves in 3–5 lobes

solitary flower
heads

fruit with
3 hooked
bristles

capitulum
1–2.5cm in
diameter

Pot Marigold
Calendula officinalis (daisy family)
H 20–50cm   June–Sept   annual to biennial

Habitat In cultivation as a garden and medicinal plant since antiquity. Europe, western Asia.

> plant has a strong, pungent scent
> stalks and leaves covered in soft down
> disc and ray florets, or just ray florets

Marigold is one of the oldest and best known herbs in Western medicine – indeed, it has been in use for so long that its origins have been lost in time. The German herbalist Hildegard von Bingen lists it as an antidote to poisoning. Elsewhere it was said to improve sight, strengthen the heart and lift the spirits. It was credited with magical powers and used in love potions. The flowers contain anti-inflammatory substances and the plant is still popular today in creams for cuts and bruises and various skin conditions. Marigold tea is used as a gargle.

leaves linear to ovate

capitulum 3–7cm across

Health tip

Anti-inflammatory gargle: use 1–2 tsp of Marigold flowers per cup, add boiling water, infuse for 10 minutes, then strain. Use as a gargle several times per day. Marigold butter as a rub for aching muscles: heat equal parts of butter and Marigold flowers until the butter has melted. The active elements will emulsify in the fat.

ray florets yellow to orange

Safflower

Carthamus tinctorius (daisy family)

H 10–60cm   July–Sept   annual

The flowers of this plant are used as a substitute for saffron – although they can only contribute the colour, not the flavour. In the past, they were also used as a fabric dye. The oil from the seeds is used in the cosmetics industry (e.g. in rouge). Folk medicine recommends the herb for digestive complaints. The oil contains essential fatty acids and helps reduce cholesterol levels.

Habitat Native to Asia Minor and India. Cultivated in the Mediterranean since antiquity, as a medicinal plant and for its dye.

> plant upright, glabrous
> capitulum with disc florets only
> spiny, thistle-like plant

capitulum 1–2cm across

leaves oval with long, sharp spines

capitulum 2–2.5cm long

spiny bracts

Cabbage Thistle

Cirsium oleraceum (daisy family)

H 50–150cm   June–Sept   herbaceous perennial

As the name implies, the young leaves and shoots of this plant can be used as a vegetable, similar to cabbage. However, its medicinal properties were largely ignored through the ages. The roots and green parts are thought to relieve cramps and toothache. Applied externally, it is said to help in the treatment of skin conditions and rheumatic complaints.

Habitat Wetland meadows, lowland forests, near water and springs. On nutrient-rich soils. Central Europe to Siberia

> indicates fertile soils
> disc florets only, pale yellow
> 2–6 capitula per stem, surrounded by bracts

cabbage-like bracts surrounding the capitulum

leaves soft, not prickly

capitulum up to 4cm long

Blessed Thistle
Cnicus benedictus (daisy family)
H 10–40cm   June–July   annual

Habitat *Native to the northern Mediterranean, formerly cultivated in central and northern Europe, occasionally naturalised.*

> stem and leaves covered in thick, bristly hairs
> flower head sits on a ring of long spiny bracts

capitulum
2–2.5cm long

During the days of the Black Death, people believed very strongly in the healing powers of this plant. It was seen as an all-heal and its virtues are praised in all major herbals from the 16th and 17th centuries. Even Shakespeare mentions the plant in *Much Ado about Nothing*. Its bitter agents aid digestion and stimulate the appetite. The herb is used in the treatment of liver and gall bladder complaints and is applied externally to ulcers and chilblains. Internal use is not advised if suffering from gastro-intestinal ulcers.

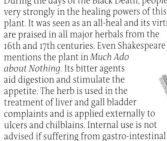

leaves clasping the stem

Health tip

Blessed Thistle tea to boost the appetite: use 1 tsp of the flowering herb per cup, add boiling water. Infuse for 5–10 minutes, then strain. Drink lukewarm and unsweetened, 2 cups per day before meals.

capitulum with disc florets only

spiny bracts

Yellow Gentian

Gentiana lutea (gentian family)
H 50–140cm   June–Aug   herbaceous perennial

The root of this plant is intensely bitter – so much so that it is used as a scientific basis to measure bitterness. It was already known in Greek antiquity, the name Gentian being derived from the Illyrian king Gentius, who is said to have discovered the plant's healing powers. Its bitter agents are utilised in conventional and herbal medicine to stimulate the secretion of digestive fluids. It is a key ingredient in bitter tonics and is used to counteract loss of appetite, aid digestion and relieve bloating and nausea. Internal use is not advised if suffering from gastro-intestinal ulcers.

Habitat Meadows and rough grassland, moors and bogs. In Alpine regions on alkaline soils. Central and southern Europe.

> calyx often split to the base along one side
> leaves opposite
> stem round, hollow

petals deeply divided

3–10 flowers in leaf axils

189

flowers on 1-cm-long stalks

root up to arm-thick

Health tip

Gentian tea to improve the appetite: use 1/2 tsp of chopped Gentian root (from a herbalist or health food shop) per cup. Add boiling water, infuse for 10–15 minutes, then strain. Drink lukewarm before meals. The tea tastes very bitter, so may benefit from the addition of some honey.

Sunflower

Helianthus annuus (daisy family)

H 100–300cm   July–Oct   annual

yellow ray florets

Habitat *Native to North America, introduced to Europe as an ornamental and crop plant, occasionally naturalised.*

> *numerous smaller cultivars*
> *leaves large, heart-shaped*
> *very large, flat capitulum*

The best-known product from this plant is probably the oil obtained from its seeds. Apart from its familiar uses in cooking and salads, it can also be used as a rub to soothe aching limbs. The yellow florets are applied externally, similar to Arnica or Marigold, to treat cuts and bruises, and are taken internally for gall bladder and liver complaints and as a fever remedy.

capitulum up to 40cm in diameter

sunflower oil is derived from the seeds

dark brown disc florets

190

Jerusalem Artichoke

Helianthus tuberosus (daisy family)

H 100–250cm   Oct–Nov   herbaceous perennial

Habitat *Native to North America, introduced to Europe as a fodder plant, naturalised in central and eastern Europe.*

> *capitulum with disc and ray florets*
> *2–3 leaves per node*

In contrast to the potato, the tubers of this plant store carbohydrates not as starch but as inulin, a polysaccharide with a low calorific value, which does not raise blood sugar levels. However, some people are not very tolerant of inulin – it tends to ferment in the gut and can cause quite severe flatulence and colic.

ray florets 3–4cm long

capitulum 4–14cm across

edible tuber

Yellow Everlasting Daisy

Helichrysum arenarium (daisy family)

H 10–30cm   July–Aug   herbaceous perennial

The dried flower heads are an ingredient in herbal tea mixes prescribed for non-inflammatory gall bladder complaints. They also give the tea a richer colour. In folk medicine, the flowers are used for their diuretic, digestive and antispasmodic properties.

Habitat *Dunes, acid grassland, pine forests. On nutrient-poor soils. Central to eastern Europe.*

> *entire plant covered in hoary down*
> *flower heads in dense clusters*
> *disc florets only*

3–40 capitula per cluster

leaves linear, downy

capitulum 6–7mm across

Mouse-ear Hawkweed

Hieracium pilosella (daisy family)

H 5–30cm   May–Oct   herbaceous perennial

According to the mediaeval German herbalist Hildegard von Bingen, Mouse-ear Hawkweed strengthens the heart and reduces bad humours. Culpeper recommends it as a cure for jaundice. In folk magic, the herb was believed to make its possessor invincible – provided it was dug out at full moon and wrapped in a white cloth.

Habitat *Meadows, rough grassland, dry woodland, rocks. Throughout most of Europe, western Asia.*

> *plant exudes a milky sap*
> *capitulum with ray florets only*
> *leaves in a rosette*

red stripes on underside of ray florets

leaves curled in during dry periods

capitulum 2–3cm across

Elecampane
Inula helenium (daisy family)
H 60–250cm   July–Aug   herbaceous perennial

Habitat Native to central Asia, introduced to Europe as a garden and medicinal plant, occasionally naturalised.

> **capitulum with disc and ray florets**
> **lower leaves 40cm long and stalked, upper leaves sessile**

capitulum
6–8cm across

The root of this plant contains active elements which, if used in excess or over long periods of time, can cause a number of unpleasant side effects, ranging from nausea and vomiting to inflamed mucous membranes and allergic reactions. Conventional medicine no longer prescribes Elecampane-based remedies, although it is still used in herbal medicine. Traditionally, it was known mainly as a cough remedy, but was also taken to expel intestinal parasites, relieve period pain, as a digestive and to treat heart conditions.

underside of leaves covered in hoary down

ray florets narrow, 3–4cm long

Did you know?
Inulin, the polysaccharide contained in Jerusalem artichokes, was first discovered in 1804, in the tubers of this plant. The species name is said to refer to Helen of Troy – from whose tears the plant is alleged to have grown.

root was a popu-
lar cough remedy

Tomato

Lycopersicon esculentum var. *esculentum* (nightshade family)
H 40–150cm   June–Oct   annual

The Tomato plant was never known as a medicinal plant in the traditional sense. The ripe fruits do, however, contain a red carotinoid pigment called lycopene, which has antioxidant properties. Recent research suggests that regular consumption of lycopene can help prevent heart disease and certain types of cancer.

Habitat *Originally from northern South America. Introduced to Europe as a crop plant.*

> stem weak, with glandular hairs
> leaves pinnate or bi-pinnate

flower star-shaped with 5–6 pointed tips

ripe fruits contain lycopene

 193

Indian Fig

Opuntia ficus-indica (cactus family)
H 200–500cm   April–July   herbaceous perennial

This species was introduced to the Mediterranean quite late in history and has therefore not played a major part in European folk medicine. Central American Indians used the liquid from the fleshy stems to treat skin infections and burns, while extracts from the flowers are said to assist in the treatment of urinary and prostate complaints. Recent studies have explored the potential of this plant as a hangover cure.

Habitat *Native to Central and North America, introduced in the Mediterranean and naturalised.*

> water is stored in the flat, oval stems
> very sharp spikes

large, flat stems

edible fruit, covered in prickly hairs

fruit egg-shaped, juicy

flower 6–10cm across

Lesser Celandine
Ranunculus ficaria (buttercup family)
H 5–20cm   March–May   herbaceous perennial

Habitat *Mixed deciduous and lowland forests, damp meadows, parks. Europe, Asia, northern Africa.*

> often forms large swathes
> stem prostrate to decumbent
> leaves heart-shaped

The fresh young leaves of this plant are rich in vitamin C and used to be eaten in salads in spring to prevent scurvy. However, as the plant matures, protoanemonin toxins accumulate, especially in the flowers and fruits. Applied externally it is a remedy for skin problems and haemorrhoids.

8–12 shiny petals

flower 2–3cm across

leaves heart-shaped

bulbils in leaf axils

Silver Ragwort
Senecio cineraria (daisy family)
H 20–80cm   May–Aug   herbaceous perennial

Habitat *Mediterranean coastal areas. Popular garden plant.*

> base of plant woody
> stem and leaves covered in white down
> capitulum with disc and ray florets

leaves feathery, covered in white down

The plant contains liver-toxic pyrrolizidine alkaloids and is therefore no longer recommended for internal use. The fresh juice extracted from the leaves was formerly known as a household remedy for eye conditions, migraines and period pain. It is still used in homeopathy in the treatment of cataracts and conjunctivitis.

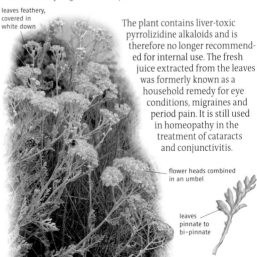

capitulum 10–15mm across

flower heads combined in an umbel

leaves pinnate to bi-pinnate

Wood Ragwort

Senecio ovatus (daisy family)

H 60–150cm   July–Sept   herbaceous perennial

Wood Ragwort contains pyrrolizidine alkaloids and is no longer recommended for internal use. In folk medicine it was once a popular remedy, used for its haemostatic properties to stem uterine bleeding. Herbal medicine used to prescribe it in teas to reduce blood sugar levels.

Habitat *Beech forests, clearings, forest glades. Central Europe, northern parts of southern Europe.*

> **numerous flower heads combined in a loose umbel**
> **capitulum with disc and ray florets**

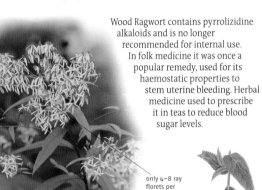

only 4–8 ray florets per flower head

leaves lanceolate, sessile

capitulum 2.5–3cm across

Canadian Goldenrod

Solidago canadensis var. *canadensis* (daisy family)

H 50–250cm   Aug–Oct   herbaceous perennial

Goldenrod has a long tradition as a medicinal herb, and this ornamental plant has similar properties to the native European species – as does the Giant Goldenrod. A tea made from the flowering herb has a diuretic action and helps prevent bladder and kidney stones. In addition, it is used to relieve mild stomach pain and colic. Goldenrod is also available in herbal preparations.

Habitat *On disturbed ground and wasteland sites. Originally from North America, introduced to Europe as a garden plant, now naturalised.*

capitulum 3–5mm long

> **numerous flower heads in large branching spikes**
> **ray florets about the same length as disc florets**

flower spikes arching

underside of leaves covered in short hairs

10–17 short ray florets

Goldenrod
Solidago virgaurea ssp. *virgaurea* (daisy family)
H 10–100cm   July–Oct   herbaceous perennial

Habitat *Open woodland, clearings, heaths and moors, rough pastures. Europe, northern Africa, western Asia.*

> 10–30 disc and 6–12 ray florets per capitulum
> lower leaves stalked, oval, upper leaves sessile

capitulum
1–2cm across

sepals overlapping

196

upper leaves linear

This plant has long been known as a vulnerary, as is reflected in its scientific name (*solidare* = to make whole) – and in the older English name 'Woundwort' – and Goldenrod does indeed contain anti-inflammatory substances (phenolic glycosides). In addition, it has diuretic properties and has been in use since the 13th century as a remedy for urinary tract infections and to prevent kidney stones. Folk medicine recommends it for catarrhs and throat infections, arthritis, gout and a range of skin conditions. However, it should not be used if suffering from oedema or heart or kidney disease.

flowers in loose panicles

Health tip
Solidago tea as a diuretic: use 1–2 tsp of Goldenrod flowers per cup, add boiling water and infuse for 15 minutes, then strain. Drink 2–4 cups per day at intervals between meals.

Common Tansy

Tanacetum vulgare (daisy family)

H 60–120cm   July–Sept   herbaceous perennial

Mediaeval herbalists recommended Tansy as a vermifuge to expel intestinal worms – and this application is still known in folk medicine. In the past, it was customary to eat the young leaves in Tansy cakes at Easter. A tea from the dried flowers was taken to relieve digestive complaints, colics and period pain. However, the herb is now considered poisonous and internal use is no longer recommended.

flower heads in small umbels of 4 or 5

yellow disc florets

leaves irregularly toothed, feathery

Habitat *Waysides, near water, rubble and wasteland sites. Throughout most of Europe and Asia.*

> *capitulum with disc florets only*
> *plant releases an aromatic fragrance when bruised*

capitulum 1cm across

Dandelion

Taraxacum Sect. Ruderale (daisy family)

H 5–40cm   April–July   herbaceous perennial

Young Dandelion leaves used to be a popular addition to fresh salads in spring. The leaves are rich in potassium and bitter agents, which stimulate the digestive system and boost the appetite. In folk medicine, Dandelion is used as a diuretic and is recommended for liver and gall bladder complaints. Homeopathy prescribes it for similar indications. Some caution is advised if suffering from gall stones.

Habitat *Meadows, pastures, parks, lawns, open ground, gardens. Worldwide.*

> *plant contains a white milky sap*
> *solitary flower head on a hollow stalk*
> *leaves in a rosette*

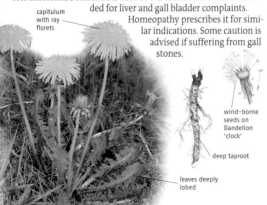

capitulum with ray florets

wind-borne seeds on Dandelion 'clock'

deep taproot

leaves deeply lobed

capitulum 2.5–4cm in diameter

Coltsfoot

Tussilago farfara (daisy family)

H 10–30cm   March–April   herbaceous perennial

Habitat *Waysides, road verges, gravel pits, near water. Europe, western Asia, northern Africa.*

> flowers open only in full sunshine
> up to 300 ray and 40 disc florets
> leaves emerge after the plant has flowered

The flowers and young leaves of Coltsfoot are rich in mucilage and have been used since antiquity as a remedy for coughs and sore throats – the scientific name *Tussilago* is derived from the Latin word *tussis* = cough. However, recent research has shown it to contain liver-toxic pyrrolizidine alkaloids and its use as a herbal remedy is therefore no longer advised. Fortunately, alkaloid-free cultivars are now available for medicinal use. It has anti-inflammatory properties and, in the past, Coltsfoot was included in a herbal tobacco mix, which was smoked to relieve asthma and catarrh.

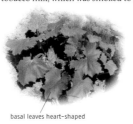

basal leaves heart-shaped

underside of leaves covered in soft down

capitulum 2–3cm across

up to 300 ray florets

flower stalk with scale-shaped leaves

up to 40 disc florets

Health tip

Coltsfoot tea as a cough remedy (only use Coltsfoot purchased from a herbalist or health food shop!): use 1 1/2 tsp of the herb per cup, add boiling water and leave to infuse for 10–15 minutes. Sweeten to taste with honey and drink several cups at intervals throughout the day.

Kidney Vetch

Anthyllis vulneraria (pea family)

H 15–30cm   May–Aug   herbaceous perennial

This plant has a long history of use as a vulnerary. Poultices from the flowers were be placed on wounds, and an infusion was used to clean out cuts and other injuries. In folk medicine, Kidney Vetch was used to treat chilblains, leg ulcers and oedema and was also recommended as a tea for oral and throat infections.

Habitat Rough grass-land and pastures, road verges, open ground. Often on chalk. Throughout most of Europe to western Asia and northern Africa.

> *plant covered in silky hairs*
> *young, yellow florets and older, brown florets within the same capitulum*

10–30 florets per capitulum

leaves on stem pinnate

sepals covered in woolly down

Birthwort

Aristolochia clematitis (birthwort family)

H 30–70cm   May–June   herbaceous perennial ☠

Due to its toxicity, this plant is no longer used in conventional or herbal medicine. In the past, it was considered a highly effective medicinal plant and had been in use since ancient Egyptian times. It was used, in particular, to assist in childbirth (hence the name), as a vulnerary and to stimulate the immune system. The plant was also credited with magical powers and still forms part of religious customs in Catholic regions of Germany.

Habitat Native to south-eastern Europe and south-eastern Asia. Introduced to Europe as a medicinal plant, occasionally naturalised in well-drained, sunny places.

> *in Britain found mainly near old monastic sites*
> *stem lightly twining*

leaves heart-shaped

flower traps insects

hairs prevent trapped insects from escaping

2–8 flowers in leaf axils

flower 3–8cm long

Common Broom
Cytisus scoparius ssp. *scoparius* (pea family)
H 50–200cm   May–June   shrub 🦋

Habitat *Heaths and moors, clearings, shrubland, along waysides and embankments, on acidic soils. Southern, western and central Europe, Britain.*

> **colonising plant on dry, open ground**
> **hairy seed pods, 6cm long**

The flowers and green parts of Broom contain alkaloids that stimulate the cardio-vascular system and have been used as a remedy for low blood pressure and to assist in childbirth. However, the composition of active elements in the plant fluctuates, and it is now used only in standardised preparations. In folk medicine, the plant was known as a depurative and a remedy for gout, rheumatic complaints, liver problems, kidney stones and jaundice. Broom remedies should not be taken when pregnant or if suffering from high blood pressure.

seed

seed pod breaks open when ripe

leaves trifoliate, sessile

style curled in

flower 2–2.5cm long

200

branches green, broom-like, with pointed tips

Did you know?
The Planta genista (the old Latin name of this plant) used to be the symbol of Geoffrey of Anjou. When he married the daughter of Henry I, mother of Henry II, the emblem of the plant was inherited by the English Plantagenet kings (1154–1399).

Woolly Foxglove

Digitalis lanata (figwort family)

H 40–100cm   June–Aug   biennial or perennial

The Woolly Foxglove has never been used in folk medicine. It contains about 80 different cardiac glycosides and is deadly poisonous! Under no circumstances should this plant be used for self-medication. In the past, medical practitioners used a powdered extract in the treatment of heart failure. Modern medicine now utilises the isolated, and sometimes chemically modified, active elements (cardenolide glycoside) – in the treatment of heart conditions.

flower stalks and calyx hairy

Habitat Shrubland and open woodland. South-eastern Europe, in central Europe cultivated as a medicinal plant.

> flowers all around the stem, facing in all directions
> corolla bulbous, with yellow-brown veins

flower 2–3cm long

201

bulbous flower

leaves linear, glabrous

lower part of corolla white, protruding

Did you know?

In order to harvest the glycosides used by the pharmaceutical industry, Woolly Foxglove is grown and harvested commercially. It yields 3 to 5 times more active elements than Purple Foxglove, and the substances are easier absorbed and metabolised quicker by the human body.

Yellow Foxglove
Digitalis lutea (figwort family)
H 30–70cm   June–Aug   herbaceous perennial

Habitat *Forest glades, clearings and paths. Mainly on alkaline soils. Western Europe, Italy.*

> stem and leaves glabrous
> flowers all facing to one side
> corolla pendent, without markings on the inside

Despite being a close relative of the other foxglove species – and containing the same active elements, albeit in a lower concentration – the Yellow Foxglove plays a much lesser part in medicine. Only in Italy, where the plant is widespread, it is more popular than Purple Foxglove. The similar-looking Large Yellow Foxglove is not used medicinally.

flower tube-shaped

corolla 2–2.5cm long

Large Yellow Foxglove with bell-shaped flower

Downy Hemp-nettle
Galeopsis segetum (mint family)
H 10–40cm   June–Aug   annual

Habitat *Rubble and waste ground, fields, forest margins. On open, stony ground. Western and central Europe.*

> flowers in whorls in the upper leaf axils
> calyx hairy, with 5 teeth

The most significant active principle of this plant is silicic acid, which may be the reason for its long-standing use in the treatment of respiratory and pulmonary diseases – an indication that dates back to Greek antiquity. In mediaeval Germany, the herb formed part of a remedy known as 'Lieber's herbs', which was taken as a cure for tuberculosis. The plant is no longer used in modern herbal medicine.

corolla pale yellow

upper petal helmet-shaped

lower petal with a dark yellow patch

leaves resembling those of Stinging Nettle

Dyers Broom

Genista tinctoria var. *tinctoria* (pea family)

H 30–60cm   June–Aug   shrub   🐝

As the name suggests, this plant used to be an important source of dye. Whilst this was obtained from the flowers only, folk medicine utilises the leaves and entire flowering shoots of the plant. The herb has diuretic properties and is thought to ease rheumatic pain and gout, and to help prevent gravel and stones. In addition, it was prescribed for period pain, constipation, liver, gall bladder and pulmonary complaints, broken bones, eczema and ulcers. It should not be used when pregnant or if suffering from high blood pressure.

Habitat *Rough grassland, fens and wetlands, forest margins, open woodland. Europe, western Asia.*

> *indicates wet ground*
> *stem upright, glabrous, ridged*
> *flowers in large spikes*

branching flower spikes

leaves linear, leaf margin entire

flowers 8–16mm long

Laburnum

Laburnum anagyroides (pea family)

H up to 8m   May–June   shrub   🐝

Despite the fact that the seeds are highly poisonous (they contain alkaloids), the plant was used medicinally in the past. The leaves were taken as an expectorant and laxative, and folk medicine utilised the seeds to induce vomiting and as a remedy for constipation, water retention and asthma. An extract from the seeds has been used as an aid to giving up smoking. Nowadays, only homeo-pathic applications remain, where the plant is indicated for diseases of the central nervous system, gastro-intestinal complaints and dizziness.

Habitat *Originally from mountain ranges of south-eastern Europe, now a popular ornamental shrub in gardens and parks. Naturalised on south-facing slopes.*

> *flowers in pendant racemes, up to 25cm long*
> *stalks and underside of leaves covered in silky down*
> *highly poisonous*

leaves trifoliate

pendant racemes

individual flower 15–20mm long

Common Toadflax

Linaria vulgaris (figwort family)

H 20–70cm   June–Oct   herbaceous perennial

Habitat Disturbed ground, fields, wasteland, railway embankments and road verges. Europe, western Asia.

> stem upright, usually unbranched
> flower closed off by a bulge on the lower petal

Throughout the Middle Ages, the Common Toadflax was believed to offer protection against witchcraft. It was placed in the cribs of children to ward off illnesses thought to be caused by evil spells. In folk medicine, it was used as a diuretic and laxative and in ointments for haemorrhoids and skin eruptions. In old herbals it is also listed as a remedy for liver and spleen complaints.

lower petal with bulge

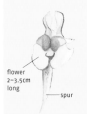

narrow, linear leaves

flower 2–3.5cm long

spur

stem densely covered in leaves

Yellow Sweet Clover

Melilotus officinalis (pea family)

H 30–100cm   June–Sept   biennial

Habitat Waysides, railway embankments, quarries, on disturbed ground and wasteland. Europe, Asia.

> up to 70 flowers per raceme
> keel of the flower much shorter than other petals
> seeds in a rounded, egg-shaped pod

The plant has been used medicinally since antiquity and is still an important ingredient in remedies for varicose veins, haemorrhoids and other venous diseases, including thrombosis. In folk medicine, it was taken in teas against coughs, varicose veins and haemorrhoids, while wraps were placed on swollen legs and joints. A homeopathic remedy is indicated for migraines and nosebleeds.

flowers in narrow racemes, 4–10cm tall

flower 5–7mm long

leaves trifoliate

Wood Sage
Teucrium scorodonia (mint family)
H 30–50cm   July–Sept   herbaceous perennial

The scientific name *Teucrium* refers to the Trojan king Teucer, who is said to have used the plant to cure diseases of the spleen. In folk medicine, the herb is primarily used as a remedy for bronchitis, but also for gastro-intestinal complaints and as a vulnerary. In the past, it was even thought to help against tuberculosis.

lower petals with 5 lobes

leaves downy

leaves decussate, stalked

Habitat Pine and oak forests, forest margins, heaths and moors. On acidic soils. Europe, northern Africa.

> plant has a pungent smell
> flowers all facing to one side
> basal leaves heart-shaped

upper petals very short

flower 1cm long

205

Field Pansy
Viola arvensis (violet family)
H 5–20cm   April–Oct   annual

flowers on long stalks

Folk medicine uses the dried flowering herb as a depurative. It is recommended as a tea for respiratory catarrhs, fevers and rheumatic pain. In herbal medicine it is used internally and externally in the treatment of skin conditions, acne, eczema and psoriasis. A homeopathic remedy is indicated for similar complaints.

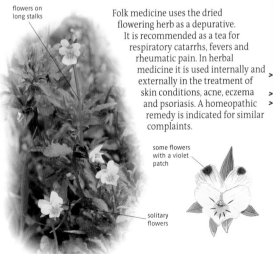

Habitat Cornfields, disturbed ground, rubble and wasteland. Europe, western Asia, northern Africa.

> common weed among winter crops
> flowers unscented
> petals yellow, upper petals white or pale violet

some flowers with a violet patch

solitary flowers

flower 1–2cm in diameter

Sweet Flag

Acorus calamus (calamus family)

H 60–120cm June–July herbaceous perennial

Habitat *Swamps, near lakes and slow-flowing rivers. Native to south-eastern Asia, in Europe naturalised.*

> **rarely bears fruits in Europe**
> **spreads through rhizomes**

Sweet Flag is one of the oldest known medicinal plants in the world. It is mentioned in ancient Persian writings as well as in the Old Testament. It is thought to have been brought to eastern Europe by the Tartars and, by the 16th century, the plant is listed in all major European herbals. The root is rich in bitter agents and essential oils and is made into bitter tonics and herbal schnapps. Folk medicine uses it externally to improve circulation and ease rheumatic pain. Do not take when pregnant of if suffering from gastro-intestinal ulcers.

root 3cm in diameter, used medicinally

leaves sword-shaped

flowers in a dense spike (spadix)

206

leaf up to 2cm wide

stem triangular, reddish at base

Did you know?

The essential oil contains an organic compound known as 'beta-asarone', which has been shown to cause cancer and genetic mutations in rats. The substance seems to occur only in certain populations of the plant.

Hazelwort

Asarum europaeum (birthwort family)

H 5–10cm   March–May   herbaceous perennial   ☠

Although highly poisonous in large doses, the root has been in medicinal use since mediaeval times. It was taken as a purgative and emetic and was recommended for sciatica and water retention – it was also used to induce abortion and should therefore be avoided during pregnancy. Modern herbal medicine uses preparations of the plant to treat asthma, coughs and bronchitis.

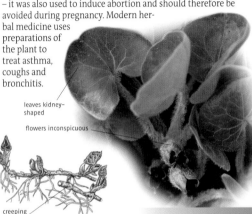

leaves kidney-shaped

flowers inconspicuous

creeping rhizomes

Habitat *Mixed and deciduous forests. On damp, often chalky soils. Central and eastern Europe, western Asia.*

> **flowers often hidden underneath leaves on the ground**
> **flowers green on the outside, reddish–brown inside**

corolla with 3–4 pointed lobes

Herb Paris

Paris quadrifolia (lily family)

H 10–30cm   May–June   herbaceous perennial   ☠

The scientific name *Paris* is said to be derived from Greek mythology and to refer to the Judgement of Paris – the plant's single berry was likened to the Apple of Discord. Old medicinal uses of the plant were similarly mythical: carrying some of the berries was thought to protect from the Black Death. The plant is still used in homeopathy, where it is prescribed for headaches and respiratory infections.

petals

single black berry

Habitat *Damp mixed deciduous forests with dense undergrowth, lowland forests. Europe, western Asia.*

> **indicates high ground-water levels**
> **usually 4 leaves, arranged cruciform around the stem**

berry up to 1cm in size

4 sepals and 4 petals

Ribwort Plantain

Plantago lanceolata (plantain family)

H 10–50cm   May–Sept   herbaceous perennial

Habitat *Rich meadows and pastures, fields, wasteland, waysides, parks. Europe, Asia.*

> **flowers in a short spike on a long, ridged stalk**
> **leaves linear, in a basal rosette**

Plantain leaves are widely known as a folk remedy for insect bites or minor injuries. The fresh juice from the leaves has antibacterial and anti-inflammatory properties, and the dried leaves can be taken as a tea to relieve respiratory catarrhs and oral or throat infections. It is also available in herbal preparations.

stamens yellow, protruding

flower spike 1cm long

leaves with 3–7 vertical veins

individual flower 2–4mm long

Common Plantain

Plantago major (plantain family)

H 5–40cm   June–Oct   herbaceous perennial

Habitat *Waysides, cracks in pavements, lawns, wasteland. Worldwide.*

> **colonising plant, resistant to trampling**
> **basal rosette, leaves often erect**

This species of plantain is slightly less popular in folk medicine than its narrow-leaved cousin. The seeds are used as a laxative and the leaves as a cough remedy and a wound herb. It is commonly used in homeopathy, where indications include skin rashes, wound pain, bed-wetting and ear infections.

narrow flower spike, up to 10cm long

leaves oval

basal leaves stalked

Mistletoe
Viscum album ssp. *album* (mistletoe family)
H 20–50cm   Feb–April   shrub   ☠

Throughout history, Mistletoe has been known as a magical plant, and legends about the plant exist in Norse as well as Greek mythology. Celtic Druids harvested Mistletoe at certain times of year using gold sickles. It was thought to offer protection from all evil. The use of Mistletoe as a Christmas decoration, and the kiss under the Mistletoe, are thought to be relics of that time. Medicinal uses include extracts or teas from the leaves, which are said to lower blood pressure and prevent arteriosclerosis. Folk medicine recommends it for epilepsy, asthma and whooping cough.

Habitat As semi-parasitic plant on deciduous trees. Often concentrated in certain areas. Europe, Asia.

> **other species use conifers as host plants**
> **male and female flowers on separate plants**

Did you know?
While some of its applications are disputed, clinical tests have shown that injections of Mistletoe extract can slow down the growth of certain types of cancer by boosting the body's own immune defence and increasing its ability to attack the cancer cells.

fruits translucent white, slightly sticky

small, inconspicuous flowers in clusters

209

translucent white berries

leaves evergreen

host tree

ANTIK

Common Ivy

Hedera helix (ivy family)

H 50–200cm Sept–Nov shrub

Habitat Mixed deciduous and lowland forests, parks, on walls. Europe, south-western Asia.

> evergreen, self-supporting climber
> flowering shoots with oval leaves

Ivy has been used as a medicinal plant since antiquity, and is often associated with the Greek god of wine, Dionysus (Bacchus). In folk medicine, Common Ivy leaf poultices were used for skin conditions and rheumatic complaints. The leaves contain active elements with expectorant and antispasmodic properties. However, the use of fresh Ivy leaves for coughs, bronchitis and asthma is no longer recommended due to its toxicity. Instead, standardised preparations are available.

berries 8–10mm in diameter

individual flower 5mm in diameter

leaves on flowering shoots oval or diamond-shaped

leaves on non-flowering shoots triangular to Maple-like

flowers in globular umbels

Did you know?

Ivy is a very important food source for wildlife. It flowers late in the year, providing essential nectar for insects in late autumn, and berries for birds throughout winter and early spring. The dense, evergreen foliage also offers shelter for nesting birds.

Silver Fir

Abies alba (pine family)
H up to 50m   May–June   tree

The essential oil derived from the needles and cones of the Silver Fir has expectorant, antibiotic and antiseptic properties. It is a common ingredient in rubs, balms, inhalants and bath extracts for coughs and colds. A homeopathic remedy is made from the young, green shoots, needles and cones and is prescribed for respiratory infections. Silver Fir remedies are not recommended if suffering from bronchial asthma.

Habitat *Mountain ranges and lower Alpine regions, up to a height of 1000m. Central and southern Europe.*

> scales on cones arranged in a spiral
> cones disintegrate at maturity, releasing the seed scales individually

cones upright

top of crown rounded

2 silvery, vertical stripes on underside of needles

211

Did you know?

A remedy known as 'Oil of Turpentine' used to be made from the resin of this tree and was a common treatment for rheumatic pain and neuralgia as well as being taken internally for bronchitis and is still used in various industries.

bark greyish-white, smooth

Cedar of Lebanon

Cedrus libani (pine family)
H up to 50m   Aug–Oct   tree

Habitat Asia Minor, Lebanon, in Europe as an ornamental tree in parks and large gardens.

> evergreen
> cones upright with a flattened top
> often multi-stemmed

The Lebanon Cedar was much revered in antiquity, and not just for its durable timber, which was used in the building of temples. The wood contains essential oils, which have expectorant properties and were inhaled or taken internally to treat infections of the respiratory system. To this day, Cedar oil is a common ingredient in chest rubs and other remedies for coughs and colds.

ripening cone

cone scales

cones 9–15cm long

needles in bunches

212

Mediterranean Cypress

Cupressus sempervirens (cypress family)
H up to 30m   April–June   tree

needles scale-like, in 4 dense rows

Habitat Eastern Mediterranean, south-western Asia, introduced and naturalised in southern Europe.

> evergreen
> columnar growth
> needles scale-shaped

The essential oil from its needles and young shoots has expectorant properties and is used in chest rubs and cough remedies for dry, persistent coughs. Because of its very strong fragrance, components of the oil are also used in perfumes, bath oils and room fresheners. A homeopathic dilution of the oil is prescribed for headaches and joint pain.

needles scale-like

cones consisting of 6–12 scales

pointed boss at the centre of each scale

cones round, up to 4cm

Common Juniper

Juniperus communis ssp. *communis* (cypress family)

H 30–100cm   Aug–Oct   shrub

Records of medicinal uses for juniper go back to Egyptian and Roman times. In the Middle Ages, its wood was burned as incense to ward off evil spirits and witchcraft, and the berries were thought to protect against the Black Death. The berries have diuretic properties, but prolonged use can lead to kidney damage (juniper berries as a kitchen spice do not pose a risk). Juniper essential oil is used in rubs to relieve rheumatic pain.
Not recommended during pregnancy and for people suffering from kidney disease.

Habitat *Heaths, moors, rough grass-land, dry woodland. Often on alkaline soils. Northern hemisphere.*

> male and female flowers usually on separate plants
> cones fleshy, more like berries

Health tip
Juniper tea to relieve heartburn, bloating and digestive disorders: use 1 level tsp of crushed Juniper berries per cup, add boiling water and infuse for 10–15 minutes, then strain. It is advisable to consult a medical practitioner before taking this remedy.

needles prickly

unripe berries green

male flowers yellow, female flowers green

213

ripe Juniper berries are blue

Savin Juniper
Juniperus sabina (cypress family)
H 100–120cm   April–May   shrub

Habitat Dry, stony and rocky ground. Mountain ranges in central and southern Europe, northern Africa, Asia.

> evergreen
> needles release a strong, unpleasant fragrance when bruised

The essential oil in the green shoots and the fruits is highly poisonous. It irritates the skin and mucous membranes and was used in mediaeval times to induce abortion. An ancient saying, 'to give birth under the Savin tree', was a euphemism for a Juniper-induced miscarriage. Folk medicine used it to treat warts, irregular periods, urinary tract infections and as a rub for rheumatic complaints.

needles scale-like, similar to Cypress needles

round cones, berry-like

cones ca. 5mm in diameter

needles scale-like

Larch
Larix decidua (pine family)
H up to 35m   March–June   tree

needles in bunches

Habitat Native to the Alps and Carpathian Mountains. Widely grown as a forest tree for its timber, and naturalised.

> deciduous
> needles in bunches of 30–40
> yellow-golden autumn colour

In Bach flower remedies, Larch is used to improve self confidence. Herbal medicine relies on the turpentine obtained from its resin. This is used externally only, in creams, emulsions, rubs and plasters for rheumatic pain, neuralgia and skin eruptions.

female flowers red-violet

male flowers greenish-yellow

scales of cones open up to release the seeds

bud

mature cones 2–4cm long

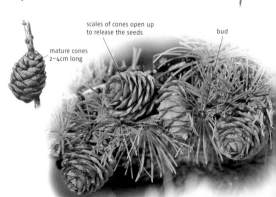

Spruce
Picea abies (pine family)
H up to 50m   April–June   tree

The young shoots and needles and their essential oil are used medicinally. They have antibacterial and expectorant properties and are used in the treatment of coughs, colds and respiratory catarrhs. Externally, the oil is applied to improve circulation and relieve rheumatic and neuralgic pain. An infusion from the young shoots was used in the past as a folk remedy for scurvy and tuberculosis. Not recommended if suffering from asthma or congestive heart failure.

Habitat *Mountain ranges up to a height of 800m. Northern and central Europe, Alps to Siberia. Common forestry tree.*

> *evergreen*
> *needles prickly, arranged in a spiral around the branch*
> *mature cones are shed intact*

female flowers

mature cones hanging

male flowers

215

Health tip

Steam inhalation for coughs and colds: add a few drops of Spruce essential oil to a bowl of steaming hot water. Drape a towel over your head and inhale the steam, then rest.

Mountain Pine

Pinus mugo ssp. *mugo* (pine family)

H 1–5m   May–July   tree

Habitat Moors and heaths in mountainous regions. Alps and Carpathian Mountains, above the treeline.

> evergreen, shrub-like growth
> able to survive under a blanket of snow
> cones mature in year two

Until 1898, Fir wood oil was listed in the British Pharmacopoeia, but was then replaced by the oil obtained from the needles of the Mountain Pine, which had been proven to be of superior quality. The indications are essentially the same as for most other conifers: as an expectorant in coughs and bronchitis, either as an inhalant or in rubs and bath oils, and as a rub for pain relief. Do not use if suffering from asthma or congestive heart failure.

female flowers at the tips of young shoots

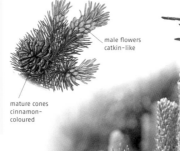

male flowers catkin-like

mature cones cinnamon-coloured

needles in pairs

216

female flowers

mature cone 2–5cm long

Health tip

Pine oil as a remedy for coughs and colds: use in the same way as Spruce essential oil. For rheumatic pain and neuralgia, use 5–10 drops of the oil and rub onto the affected areas several times a day.

Maritime Pine

Pinus pinaster (pine family)
H up to 40m   April–June   tree

Oil of turpentine is distilled from the resin of this tree. This is used as an inhalant for chronic bronchitis and as a rub for rheumatic complaints and neuralgia. The residue from the distillation process yields a substance known as rosin (or colophony), which is used, amongst other things, to prepare the bows of string instruments.

male flowers

mature cone

long needles, up to 25cm

Habitat Coastal areas, sandy, lime-free soils, western Mediterranean.

> evergreen
> bark of older trees fissured
> needles always in pairs

cones in groups of 3–8, star-shaped around the stem

8–22cm long

217

Scots Pine

Pinus sylvestris var. *sylvestris* (pine family)
H up to 40m   May–June   tree

The oil is used in the same way as that of other conifers – as an inhalant for coughs and colds, in scented bath oils and as a rub for circulatory disorders. In folk medicine, the young shoots are boiled in water to obtain a syrupy extract, which can be used for the same purposes.

1–3 female flowers at the tips

ripening cones reddish-green

Habitat Dunes, rocks, heaths and moors. On well-drained soils. Common forestry tree.

> evergreen
> female flowers at the tips of new shoots
> male flowers below female ones

cones rounded, on short stalks

mature cones hanging

Common Yew
Taxus baccata (yew family)
H up to 15m   March–May   tree   🐿

Habitat Ancient wood-
land. In parks, gardens
and cemeteries, often
in clipped hedges and
as topiaries.

> evergreen
> male and female flowers
  on separate plants
> needles dark green, soft,
  in 2 rows

Yews are very slow-growing trees and large yews are often
remnants of ancient plantations. The Druids used to plant yews
near sacred places and made staffs and wands from its wood. Once
Christianity replaced the ancient religions, the Common Yew
became associated with cemeteries, though it is also a popular
garden plant and ideal for clipped hedges and topiaries. Virtually
all parts of the plant are highly poisonous, but it was still used in
folk medicine to expel intestinal worms, for irregular periods and
in the treatment of heart conditions.

female
flowers
green

seeds dark
green to black

male flowers
yellow

fruits berry-like, red
fleshy coat surrounding
the seed

Did you know?
*Taxol, a substance
obtained from the
bark of the Pacific Yew
(Taxus brevifolia) has
been shown to inhibit
cell growth and is used
in the treatment of
certain types of cancer.
The substance has now
also been isolated
from the leaves of
other yew species.*

Common Alder

Alnus glutinosa (birch family)
H up to 25m   March–April   tree

unripe
female cones

Alder bark is used only in folk medicine and homeopathy. The former utilises its tannins, and a decoction from the bark was used as a gargle for oral and throat infections or was administered in enemas for intestinal bleeding. In homeopathy it is indicated for skin diseases.

Habitat *Lowland forests, along rivers and streams, near springs. Throughout Europe and into Siberia, northern Africa.*

> *flowers (catkins) appear before the leaves*
> *fruits in small cones*
> *leaves alternate*

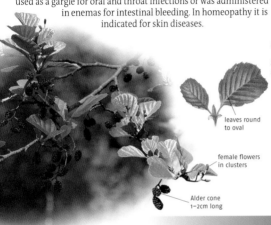

female
flowers

leaves round
to oval

female flowers
in clusters

male flowers
in catkins

Alder cone
1–2cm long

Silver Birch

Betula pendula (birch family)
H up to 25m   April–May   tree

Dried Silver Birch leaves are mildly diuretic, without over-stimulating the kidneys, and are recommended for urinary tract infections. In folk medicine, an infusion from the leaves is used to ease rheumatic pain and gout, and a decoction from the leaves and bark is applied as a skin tonic. The fresh sap, harvested in early spring, was recommended as a remedy for thinning hair.

Habitat *Mixed and deciduous forests, rough grassland, heaths and moors, wasteland. Europe, western Asia.*

> *deciduous*
> *male catkins pendant*
> *tiny seeds with 2 small, transparent wings on either side*

female flowers
initially
upright, later
drooping

female flowers
green

male
flowers
yellowish-
brown

leaves almost
diamond-
shaped

male catkins
10cm long

Sweet Chestnut
Castanea sativa (beech family)
H up to 30m   June   tree

Habitat Native to south-western Asia and southern Europe, naturalised in Britain since Roman times.

> male flowers in long upright catkins
> female flowers below male ones
> very spiky fruit shell

Chestnuts are not just a popular stuffing ingredient for the Christmas turkey, in the tree's native regions they are also known as a gentle household remedy for diarrhoea. However, the real medicinal power is in the leaves, which are rich in tannins and are known in folk medicine as a remedy for coughs and sore throats (as a gargle), circulatory problems, aching legs and diarrhoea.

male flowers in long catkins, 15–20cm

female flowers at base of male catkin

edible seeds

leaves up to 30cm long

Health tip

Chestnut leaf tea for respiratory complaints: use 2 tsp of finely chopped leaves per cup, add cold water and bring to the boil. Strain immediately and leave to cool. Drink 2–3 cups per day at intervals.

220

old male catkin

spiky fruit shell

Carob

Ceratonia siliqua (pea family)
H 2–10m   July–Sept   large shrub or small tree

The seeds of this tree have a constant weight of 0.18 grams – the equivalent of 1 carat – and have in the past been used to assess the value of jewels. A flour extracted from the seeds is largely indigestible and is used as a bulking and gelling agent in baby and diet foods and pharmaceutical products. In some parts of the world, the seed shells are used as a household remedy for diarrhoea.

Habitat Maquis, rocky slopes. On nutrient-poor soils. Mediterranean region, western Asia, northern Africa.

> evergreen
> leaves even-pinnate
> flowers grow directly from the branches

fruits

seed pods up to 20cm long

flowers grow directly from branches

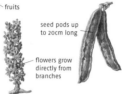

flower without petals

221

Beech

Fagus sylvatica (beech family)
H up to 40m   April–May   tree

Beech charcoal, or a tar distilled from the wood (known as 'creosote'), was used in folk medicine to treat skin conditions and rheumatic complaints. The fruits, the creosote and the charcoal (under the name of Carbo vegitabilis) are also used in homeopathy. Although the fruits contain an edible oil, the seeds themselves can cause stomach pain and nausea.

leaves oval, very smooth

male catkins round, on long stalks

Habitat Forests. On loamy, alkaline soils. Central and western Europe including Britain, mountain ranges in southern Europe.

> deciduous
> female flowers in pairs on short upright stalks
> nuts (known as 'mast') in a spiny husk consisting of 4 lobes

edible Beech nuts (beechmast)

male flowers in pendant clusters (catkins) on long stalks

Fig Tree
Ficus carica (mulberry family)
H 2–10m   June–Sept   small tree

Habitat *Native to the Mediterranean, Asia Minor and north-western India, cultivated as a crop and garden plant in temperate regions.*

> deciduous tree
> flowers hidden in a fleshy green shell resembling the fruit
> green parts and unripe fruits contain milky white sap

The Fig Tree has played an important role throughout history, and not just in the context of Adam and Eve's proverbial fig leaf. Fig Trees have been grown for their fruits since the days of the Assyrians. In the Arabic world, the fruits are considered an aphrodisiac. Fresh figs are a gentle laxative and have been used as a household remedy for kidney and bladder stones. The leaves are applied in poultices to wounds, and a decoction is used to relieve painful haemorrhoids or is taken internally for digestive complaints and to expel intestinal worms.

flowers look like unripe fruits

leaves with 3–5 lobes

ripe fig

ripening fruit on the tree

Did you know?
Fig leaves can be used in cooking. They contain enzymes that help tenderise meat, and can be used to wrap fish before grilling. A liquid extract from fig leaves has been shown to have antidiabetic properties.

Common Ash

Fraxinus excelsior (olive family)
H up to 40 m   April–May   tree

The leaves and bark of the Common Ash are used in folk medicine and homeopathy, though not in conventional medicine. The leaves contain tannins, mucilage and plant acids. They are taken in teas as a diuretic and gentle laxative, to relieve rheumatic complaints, gout and stones, and are used to treat slow-healing wounds.

Habitat Mixed and lowland forests, along rivers and streams. Europe, Asia Minor to Caucasus.

> deciduous
> colonising tree, also on dry ground
> flowers appear before leaves

leaflet

leaves odd-pinnate

Ash fruits, known as 'keys'

flowers in dense clusters

bunches of Ash keys

223

Ginkgo

Ginkgo biloba (ginkgo family)
H up to 30m   March–April   tree

Ginkgo leaves are prescribed in Traditional Chinese Medicine for asthmatic complaints. In Western herbal medicine, preparations from Ginkgo leaves are sold as a herbal supplement, said to stimulate brain activity. Studies have shown that Gingko improves blood flow to the brain, but claims that this may assist in the treatment of Alzheimer's disease have yet to be scientifically proven.

distinctive, fan-shaped leaves

Habitat Native to China, grown worldwide as an ornamental tree.

> deciduous, golden-yellow autumn colour
> botanically related to conifers, despite being a deciduous, broad leaved tree
> male and female flowers on separate plants

ripe fruits round, 2–3cm in diameter

leaves divided into 2 triangular lobes

leaves tough, papery

Sea Buckthorn

Hippophae rhamnoides ssp. *rhamnoides* (oleaster family)
H up to 5m   March–May   shrub

> **thorny shrub**
> **male and female flowers on separate plants**
> **individual flowers inconspicuous, in dense clusters in the leaf axils**

male flower with 2 sepals

Health tip

Sea Buckthorn jam: place 150g of freshly picked berries in a saucepan with a little water and 100g sugar. Bring to the boil and cook until the berries are soft and mushy. Strain through a sieve and bring back to boil. Fill into jam jars and leave to cool. The berries can also be used in mixed jams.

The berries of Sea Buckthorn are unusually rich in a number of vitamins, notably C, E, F, some B vitamins and pro-vitamin A. In addition, they contain fruit acids and a rare and valuable fatty acid (palmitoleic acid), which has been used in Russia to treat radiation damage and promote wound healing. In India, the oil is known as a medicine for pulmonary complaints. Although the raw berries are unpalatable, their juice is used in Western medicine as an antioxidant health supplement to prevent colds and boost vitamin-C supply, and is added to fruit juices and tinned fruits.

berries 7–8mm in diameter

underside of leaves covered in silvery down

Walnut Tree

Juglans regia (walnut family)
H up to 25m   May   tree

Walnuts are mainly known for their edible seeds, though in the past the green fruit shells and leaves were also used as a dye and applied medicinally. They contain tannins and were used in poultices and rinses for skin problems, eczema, athlete's foot and as a vulnerary. A tea from the leaves was taken as a household remedy for stomach and digestive complaints. The green fruit husks have been utilised in the cosmetics industry for hair dyes and self-tanning products.

Habitat *Originally from the Balkans and south-western Asia, cultivated throughout Europe for its fruits.*

> deciduous
> 2–3 female flowers at tips of shoots
> leaves alternate, pinnate

Health tip

Walnut leaf foot soak: add 200ml of cold water to 4–6 tsp of chopped Walnut leaves. Bring to the boil and simmer for 3–5 minutes, then leave to infuse for a further 15 minutes. Strain and add to your footbath. Used several times per day this will combat sweaty feet and odour.

walnut in green fruit husk

catkins ca. 10cm long

male catkins pendent

ripening walnut on tree

225

leaflets long, oval

Mastic Tree
Pistacia lentiscus (cashew family)
H up to 8m   March–June   shrub or small tree

leaves
even-
pinnate

leaf rachis
winged

Habitat Dry forests, maquis, garigue. Mediterranean regions.

> evergreen
> male and female flowers on separate plants
> black berries, 4mm in size

Mastic, the resin from this tree, is obtained from incisions made into the bark. It was once used as a glue for plasters and false beards. In its native countries, mastic is still used as a folk remedy for coughs, bronchitis, stomach complaints and diarrhoea. The leaves are said to help lower blood pressure.

male flower reddish

male flowers in small racemes

leaves leathery

Oaks
Quercus (beech family)
H 30–50m   May   tree

leaves lobed

Habitat Mixed and deciduous forests, as solitary tree in fields and pastures, in hedgerows.

> acorns of Pedunculate Oak (English Oak) on stalks, sessile on Sessile Oak
> flowers emerge before the leaves
> leaves of Pedunculate Oak on short stalks, with auricles, leaves of Sessile Oak on longer stalks, without auricles

The Bach flower remedy oak is recommended for people who struggle on against adversity – it is said to instil in its user the strength of the oak tree. The bark contains tannins, and its astringent and haemostatic properties have been known since antiquity. It is used externally in the treatment of itchy skin conditions, haemorrhoids and wounds and as a gargle for oral and throat infections.

deeply fissured bark

acorns of Pedunculate Oak on long stalks

flowers of Sessile Oak

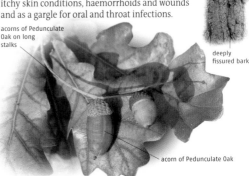

acorn of Pedunculate Oak

Butcher's Broom

Ruscus aculeatus (lily family)

H 10–80cm   Oct, Feb–April   shrub

flower on cladode

The name Butcher's Broom is thought to be derived from the fact that butchers used to cover their meat with this plant to protect it from mice. The root has antibacterial and diuretic properties. An extract from the root is used in medications for venous insufficiency. In folk medicine, the plant was used as an anti-inflammatory and diuretic.

Habitat Forests, shrubland. Mediterranean, western France and Belgium, south-western Asia.

> evergreen shrub
> male and female flowers on separate plants
> flowers on leaf-shaped, spiny stalks (cladodes)

leaf-shaped stalk (cladode)

flower

dried root is used medicinally

bright red berries

Small-leaved Elm

Ulmus minor (elm family)

H up to 40m   March–April   tree

In French folk medicine, elm was valued as a remedy for chronic skin diseases. The bark from the young branches contains tannins and was used to treat oral and throat infections, diarrhoea, digestive disorders and water retention. The Bach flower remedy elm is recommended for people who 'feel overwhelmed with responsibility or a sense of inadequacy'.

Habitat Lowland forests, edges of fields, hedgerows, quarries. Southern and central Europe, south-western Asia, north-western Africa, along roads and lanes.

> deciduous
> flowers appear before the leaves
> leaf base asymmetrical

seed membrane notched

seed near edge of membrane

seeds embedded in winged fruit

flowers in dense clusters

White Willow

Salix alba var. *alba* (willow family)
H up to 30m   April–May   shrub or tree

Habitat *Alongside lakes, streams, ditches and rivers, on flood-plains. Europe, Asia.*

> • *often pollarded in the past*
> • *male and female flowers on separate plants*
> • *flowers appear with the leaves*

Willow bark is famously known for its salicin content, the substance from which aspirin was first derived. A decoction from the bark has been used since ancient times to relieve headaches, rheumatic, arthritic or neuralgic pain and gout, to reduce fever and ease the symptoms of colds and flu. In Bach flower remedies, willow is recommended for people who feel resentful and bitter. Avoid willow preparations during pregnancy.

underside of leaves silvery

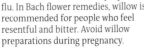

female catkin

female flowers with glabrous ovary

male catkin

seeds covered in woolly down

Health tip

Willow bark tea for stomach and digestive complaints: use 1 tsp of crushed willow bark per cup and add cold water. Heat gently until just simmering, then remove from the heat and leave to infuse for 5 minutes. Strain, sweeten to taste.

Common Grape Vine

Vitis vinifera ssp. *vinifera* (grape family)
H up to 10m   June–July   climbing shrub

Wine played an important role in all ancient cultures and the cultivation of grapes for wine-making spread to southern and central Europe during Greek and Roman times. Vine leaves contain flavonoids and tannins and were used in folk medicine to treat skin conditions and to stem bleeding. Modern herbal medicine recommends vine leaf extract to strengthen the blood vessels. The grapes act as a gentle laxative and are also a useful restorative that supports the body through illness.

Habitat *Lowland forests, riverbanks. Native to south-eastern Europe, western Asia, cultivated worldwide in a vast range of varieties, occasionally naturalised.*

Did you know?

Both red and white wine contains phenolic compounds with powerful antioxidant properties. It increases levels of 'good' HDL cholesterol in the blood, reducing the risk of arteriosclerosis and heart disease – if consumed in moderation!

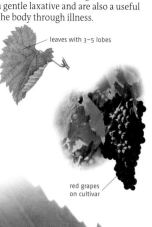

leaves with 3–5 lobes

red grapes on cultivar

> deciduous climbing plant
> male and female flowers on separate plants in wild varieties

flowers inconspicuous, fragrant

229

flowers in a branched raceme

Lady's Mantle
Alchemilla xanthochlora (rose family)
H 10–70cm   May–Sept   herbaceous perennial

Habitat *Meadows, pastures, shrubland, forest paths, ditches. On damp soils. Throughout Europe.*

> leaf margins exude water in humid weather
> leaf surface covered in fine down, water pearls off

2–3mm across

individual flower star-shaped

The name Lady's Mantle refers to the shape of its leaves, which were thought to resemble the cloak worn by the Virgin Mary. Throughout history, the plant was revered for its healing properties, as a vulnerary and for a number of women's ailments, such as period pain, vaginal discharge and problems associated with the menopause.

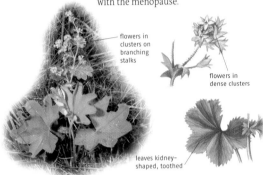

flowers in clusters on branching stalks

flowers in dense clusters

leaves kidney-shaped, toothed

Oats
Avena sativa (grass family)
H 60–150cm   June–Aug   annual

Habitat *Originally from the Mediterranean, cultivated as a crop plant, occasionally naturalised along waysides and on waste ground.*

> tufted at base
> spikelets with 2 florets and a long awn
> loosely branching inflor-escence, 15–30cm tall

spikelets pendent

Oat porridge is a healthy and nourishing breakfast that is gentle on the stomach, can lower cholesterol and is a remedy for diarrhoea. Folk medicine recommends a decoction of Oat straw strained into the bathwater to soothe itchiness and eczema and relieve rheumatic pain and gout.
A modern herbal preparation known as 'Green Oats' is sold as an aphrodisiac.

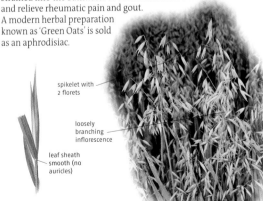

spikelet with 2 florets

loosely branching inflorescence

leaf sheath smooth (no auricles)

Hemp

Cannabis sativa (hemp family)

H 30–250cm   July–Oct   annual

Hemp has been used since ancient times as a medicinal and narcotic plant. The earliest records of its medicinal use date back to Chinese texts from 2700 BC – and it is still used in Traditional Chinese Medicine. In Europe, on the other hand, it was primarily known and cultivated for its fibre. The flowers of the female plants contain tetrahydrocannabinol (THC). Its anti-emetic properties are used to treat cancer patients undergoing chemotherapy. It also suppresses pain and improves the appetite.

Habitat *Native to south-eastern Asia, cultivated worldwide as a crop plant for oil and fibre.*

> low-THC varieties are grown commercially for fibre
> male and female flowers on separate plants

male flower

231

loosely grouped at top of stem

male flowers in clusters

female flowers contain THC

upright in the leaf axils

leaves palmate, in 3–9 lobes

leaf margins coarsely toothed or serrate

Did you know?

Although its use as a recreational drug remains illegal in many countries, there is increasing demand for Hemp as a renewable resource. Under European legislation, Hemp grown for fibre must be certified to have THC levels below 0.3%.

Sand Sedge
Carex arenaria (sedge family)
H 10–50cm   May–June   herbaceous perennial

Habitat *Heaths and moors, dunes, on sandy soils. Northern, western and central Europe.*

> **extensive, creeping rhizomes**
> **stem triangular**
> **plant releases an aromatic fragrance when bruised**

Sand Sedge was discovered as a medicinal plant as late as the 18th century. At the time, the rhizomes were thought to be a cure for syphilis – as a substitute for the more expensive sarsaparilla (Smilax root). It has diuretic and diaphoretic properties and was used in folk medicine as a depurative and in the treatment of rheumatic complaints, gout and skin disorders.

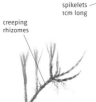

individual spikelets 1cm long

creeping rhizomes

flowers in spikes, 4–6cm tall

flower stalk

232

False Hemp
Datisca cannabina (Datisca family)
H 1–2m   June–Sept   herbaceous perennial

Habitat *Riversides, forests. Cyprus, Crete, south-western Asia as far as the Himalayas.*

> **plant looks similar to Hemp**
> **male and female flowers on separate plants**

Due to its limited distribution, this plant has never played a major part in European folk medicine. Nevertheless, an active principle derived from the roots and green parts of this plant is now sold in herbal preparations: a yellow dye known as datiscin, which is thought to have a similar effect to insulin. The plant is also used in homeopathy in the treatment of diabetes.

flowers in racemes

flowers

leaves odd-pinnate

flowers in branching racemes

Couch Grass

Elymus repens (grass family)

H 30–150cm   June–Aug   herbaceous perennial

The English herbalist John Gerard (1597) described Couch Grass as 'an unwelcome guest to fields and gardens, yet its physical virtues do recompense those hurts'. This assessment still applies today. The rhizomes have diuretic properties and are used in the treatment of urinary tract infections, such as cystitis, and in folk medicine also for bronchial infections, gout and rheumatic complaints and as a laxative. Do not use if suffering from oedema or heart or kidney disease.

Habitat Disturbed ground, gardens, fields, riverbanks. Europe, Asia.

> spreads via underground rhizomes
> flower spike in 2 rows

spikelets 10cm long

233

Health tip

Couch Grass root tea for urinary tract infections: use 2–3 tsp of rhizomes per cup, add boiling water and infuse for 10 minutes. Strain and drink up to 4 cups per day.

rhizomes

spikelet

spikelets in 2 rows, spread-out

yellow stamens

Cypress Spurge
Euphorbia cyparissias (spurge family)
H 10–30cm   April–Aug   herbaceous perennial

Habitat *Rough grassland, lawns, waysides and road verges, wasteland. On dry, alkaline soils. Throughout Europe.*

> **plant contains a white, milky sap (latex)**
> **4 crescent-shaped nectaries**
> **flowers inconspicuous**

The poisonous sap irritates the skin and mucous membranes and is even thought to contain carcinogenic substances. Avoid contact with the eyes and do not use this plant for self-medication! In the past, the root was pickled in vinegar and used as a household remedy for constipation and toothache, and the milky sap was applied to warts.

yellow-green bracts

leaves alternate

flowers in small umbels

Barley
Hordeum vulgare (grass family)
H 50–150cm   May–June   annual

Habitat *Only known in cultivation.*

> **malt derived from Barley is one of the key ingredients in beer-making**
> **green plant with a glaucous bloom**

Although a major food crop in many parts of the world, the majority of the Barley harvested in the UK goes towards the production of beer, whiskey and malted drinks. In medicine, Barley is used in the form of malt extract. A decoction of pearl barley is a nutritious and demulcent drink and a remedy for respiratory and urinary catarrhs.

spikelets in 4 rows, spikes deflexed

leaves clasping the stem, with auricles

ripe grain

awns up to 15cm long

Hops

Humulus lupulus (hemp family)
H 200–400cm   July–Aug   herbaceous perennial

Only the unfertilised female plants are cultivated for beer-making. The bitter agents accumulated in their flower heads (known as 'cones' or 'strobiles') are responsible for the drink's characteristic taste. In herbal medicine, the plant is used as a mild sedative and sleep aid. Folk medicine recommends a tea made from Hops for loss of appetite and as a digestive. In mediaeval times it was used to curb sexual desire. Skin contact with the plant can cause dermatitis in some people.

Habitat Lowland forests, forest margins, wasteland sites, on fences, mainly in cultivation. Throughout Europe, south-western Asia, North America.

> male and female flowers on separate plants
> climbing and trailing plant

thin, thread-like stigmas

female hop cone

male flowers in panicles, 5–10cm long

lower leaves with 3–5 lobes

upper leaves simple

235

Health tip

Hop tea as a natural sleep aid: use 1–2 tsp of Hop flowers per cup, add hot water and infuse for 10 minutes. Strain and add honey to taste. Drink before going to bed. The Hop flowers can be mixed in a ratio of 1:1 with Valerian.

hop cones (female flowers) pendant

Dog's Mercury
Mercurialis perennis (spurge family)
H 15–30cm   April–May   herbaceous perennial ☠

Habitat Forests with rich undergrowth. On damp soils. Europe, south-western Asia.

> indicates high ground-water levels
> male and female flowers on separate plants

female flower with enlarged ovary

Dog's Mercury is mentioned as a laxative and diuretic as early as the 4th/5th century BC. In mediaeval times, it was used to treat illnesses thought to have been caused by witchcraft. In some countries, the plant was even believed to assist in the conception of a male child. A decoction was used externally for women's complaints, ear and eye problems, warts and sores. Homeopathy prescribes it for irregular periods, and its annual form (*M. annua*) is used in the treatment of rheumatic complaints.

male flowers in upper leaf axils

leaves oval, toothed

stem unbranched

236

flowers almost sessile

annual form

stem branching

Did you know?

According to legend, the plant's medicinal virtues were revealed by the god Mercury. In Norse mythology the herb was sacred to Odin (Wotan) and, in order for its magic to be effective, it had to be picked on a Wednesday, the day devoted to Odin.

Pellitory-of-the-Wall

Parietaria officinalis (nettle family)
H 30–100cm   June–Oct   herbaceous perennial

This plant has been used in folk and herbal medicine for centuries. The tea has a diuretic action and was taken for inflammations of the urinary tract, to ease rheumatic pain and to prevent kidney disease. In addition, the plant was used in the past for cleaning glass and copper containers.

Habitat Lowland forests, riverbanks and lakesides, on walls, rubble and waste ground. On damp, nutrient-rich soils. Mediterranean and central Europe.

> *Plant resembles the Stinging Nettle, but without stinging hairs*
> *leaves lanceolate (pointed at both ends)*
> *flowers in clusters in the leaf axils*

dense clusters of flowers in leaf axils

leaves 5–10cm long

leaves alternate

individual flower 1–2mm across

flowers with 4 petals

Dark Psyllium

Psyllium afrum (plantain family)
H 10–40cm   April–July   annual

Psyllium husks are extremely rich in mucilage and swell up to several times their size on contact with water. They act as a gentle, bulk-forming laxative and are recommended for constipation and painful haemorrhoids, but also to improve stool consistency in watery diarrhoea.

Habitat Fields, along waysides, garigue. Mediterranean region, south-western Asia.

> *grown commercially in France*
> *plant covered in glandular hairs*

anthers protruding

leaves downy

flowers in globular clusters

seed shells canoe-shaped

Castor Oil Plant

Ricinus communis (spurge family)

H 50–500cm   Feb–Sept   annual to biennial or perennial

Habitat *Originally from tropical Africa, naturalised in the Mediterranean, in central and northern Europe grown as a garden plant.*

> flowers in a tall spike, female flowers at the top, male flowers further down
> leaves palmate

The seeds of this plant contain a toxic protein, which has to be removed before processing the oil. Castor oil is a strong laxative, which was already known to the ancient Egyptians, as is evident from archaeological finds and ancient texts. In Europe it has been used medicinally since the Middle Ages.

female flowers with red stigmas

leaves deeply lobed

female flowers in a large terminal spike

male flowers yellow

Common Wheat

Triticum aestivum (grass family)

H 50–160cm   June   annual

Habitat *Cultivated worldwide as a crop, origins unknown.*

> root as deep as 1m
> awns very short or missing

The starch from the seeds is used in pharmaceutical products as a bulking and gelling agent (in powders, pastes and pills). Wheatgerm oil contains valuable fatty acids and vitamin E. Wheat bran is rich in fibre and, added to bathwater, it soothes itchy and weeping skin conditions.

ripe grain

spikelets in 4 regular rows

base of leaf with auricles

Stinging Nettle

Urtica dioica (nettle family)

H 30–15cm   July–Oct   herbaceous perennial

Historic herbals often list the Stinging Nettle as a cure for dropsy. Folk medicine later used it to treat rheumatism, gout, muscle weakness and skin complaints. The active components in its leaves have diuretic properties, and modern herbal medicine recommends nettle tea for infections of the urinary tract. Avoid if suffering from oedema, or heart or kidney disease.

Habitat Waysides, rubble and wasteland, ditches, forest margins. Northern hemisphere.

> indicates nitrogen-rich soil
> stem square, angular
> male and female flowers on separate plants

leaves with stinging hairs

male flowers in upright panicles

239

female flowers in drooping panicles

close-up of stinging hairs

Health tip

Nettle tea to flush out the urinary tract: use 3–4 tsp of Stinging Nettle leaves per cup, add boiling water, infuse for 10 minutes, then strain. Drink 3–4 freshly made cups throughout the day.

Male Fern

Dryopteris filix-mas (buckler fern family)
H 30–120cm   herbaceous perennial

Habitat Shady ground in forests. On damp soils. *Europe, Asia, America.*

> leaf fronds evergreen, in a rosette
> pinnae margins crenate with rounded teeth
> sporangia (sori) contained in a kidney-shaped indusium

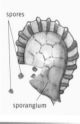

spores

sporangium

sporangia (sori)

240

Did you know?

In mediaeval times, people were looking in vain for the 'fern seeds'. Apparently, to obtain them, one had to make a pact with the devil. Anyone in possession of the elusive commodity would never run out of money and also have the power to become invisible.

sporangia on fertile fronds

Male Fern (or Male Shield Fern) has been known since antiquity as a remedy for tapeworm and intestinal parasites. The root was used to paralyse the worms, which were then flushed out with the help of a laxative. This method was still practised into early modern times. However, it was not without risk: overdosing the fern root often led to blindness or even death. It is therefore no longer advised. A homeopathic remedy under the name of Filix mas is prescribed for impaired vision. The leaf fronds are occasionally used as an ingredient in digestive remedies.

root with fern crozier (the coiled leaf)

Common Polypody

Polypodium vulgare (polypody family)
H 10–40cm   herbaceous perennial   🐝

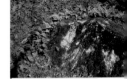

The root of this fern contains a substance known as osladin, which is 3,000 times sweeter than sugar. For this, it has been used as an adulterant in liquorice sweets. In folk medicine it is used as an expectorant and mild laxative. In the past, it was also recommended for diseases of the spleen and lungs.

Habitat Shaded walls and rocks, on the bark of trees. Usually on lime-free soils. Europe, Asia, America.

> **leaf fronds grow in a double row along a creeping rhizome, not evergreen**
> **yellow sori**

leaf fronds pinnate

pinnae margins entire or crenate

creeping rhizome

Common Clubmoss

Lycopodium clavatum (clubmoss family)
H 5–30cm   herbaceous perennial   🐝

The fine, powdery spores were used in the past by pharmacists as a dusting powder to stop pills from sticking together. In addition, they were applied to wounds and skin conditions and used as a lubricant. In folk medicine, the green fronds were recommended as a diuretic. Internal use is no longer advised, however, as the plant contains poisonous alkaloids. It is still prescribed in homeopathy.

Habitat Heaths and moors, bogs, coniferous forests. On acidic soils. Northern hemisphere.

> **creeping stem, spreading but not much branched**
> **leaves arranged in a spiral around the stem**

2–3 strobili per stalk

long-stalked strobilus

creeping stem

leaflets with a white tip

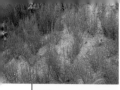

Field Horsetail

Equisetum arvense (horsetail family)
H 20–50cm   herbaceous perennial

Habitat Fields, waysides, disturbed ground, forests. On moist, nutrient-rich soils. Northern hemisphere.

> brown fertile stems in spring
> sterile green stems in summer
> both sterile and fertile stems of the poisonous Marsh Horsetail are green

sterile shoot

The stems of Field Horsetail are extremely rich in silicic acid, which gives the plant its peculiar stability. For this, it was used in the past to polish metal and hardwood. It also contains a natural fungicide protecting against mildew. The dried herb has been used medicinally since antiquity for its diuretic and astringent action, and horsetail tea is still prescribed by modern herbalists for urinary tract infections or as a gargle for throat infections. In folk medicine, horsetail is known as a remedy for rheumatic complaints.

cone-like spike (strobilus) containing the sporangia

poisonous Marsh Horsetail: toothed sheath is longer than first section of lateral shoot

toothed sheath ends below first section of lateral shoot

lateral shoot

toothed sheath on stem sections

Health tip

Horsetail wrap to ease rheumatic pain: add 1 litre of boiling water to 3–5 tbsp of the herb and leave to infuse for 1 hour, then strain. Add to the bathwater or use in wraps.

fertile stem of Field Horsetail

Iceland Moss

Cetraria islandica (lichen family)
H 10cm   thallophyte

Despite its name, Iceland Moss is actually really a lichen, its healing properties having first been discovered by the Icelandic people. It contains mucilage and lichen acid. The former soothes coughs and sore throats, the latter has antibiotic properties. Folk medicine recommends a tea made from Iceland Moss as a digestive.

Habitat *Arctic regions, mountain ranges of both hemispheres.*

> *thallus grows flat on the ground*
> *branches ending in lobes with fringed edges*
> *lichens are a symbiotic association of fungi and green algae*

underside of
thallus
whitish-grey

thallus fresh-green
when moist

branching thallus

Irish Moss

Chondrus crispus (red algae family)
H 5-20cm   thallophyte

Irish 'Moss' is a seaweed or red alga. It is also known as 'carrageen' and is used in dried form, for its mucilage content, in the treatment of coughs, catarrhs and other respiratory diseases, as well as for digestive complaints and diarrhoea. The mucilage itself is indigestible and is used as a thickening agent in food, cosmetics and pharmaceutical products.

Habitat *Rocky coasts of the Atlantic, grows just below the water surface.*

> *thallus purplish-red to green*
> *attached to the rock via a discoid holdfast*

dried thallus

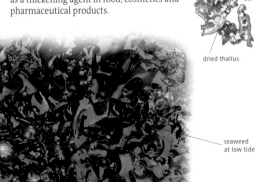

seaweed
at low tide

branching thallus

Bladder Wrack

Fucus vesiculosus (brown algae family)
H 10–80cm   thallophyte

Habitat *Rocks in the intertidal zone. Atlantic coast, North and Baltic Seas.*

> *often washed ashore*
> *thallus olive-green to yellowish-brown, branching*

In some coastal areas, Bladder Wrack is so abundant that it is utilised in agriculture as fertiliser or animal fodder. It is rich in iodine, which the plant extracts from the seawater. Iodine stimulates the thyroid gland, and Bladder Wrack used to be prescribed for underactive thyroid. However, since its iodine levels vary and a number of side effects have been reported, its medicinal use has now been superseded by more effective remedies.

air-filled vesicles

thallus with central vein

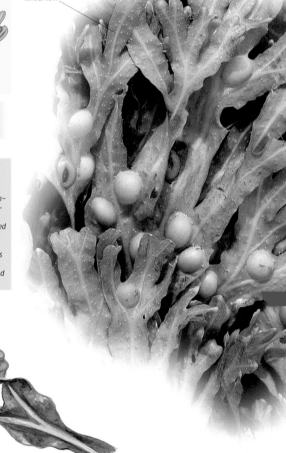

244

Did you know?

With the rising popularity of health spas, a number of spas, a number now offer thalasso-therapy – health and beauty treatments based on products derived from the sea. A variety of wraps, masks, scrubs and creams are made from Bladder Wrack and other seaweeds.

conceptacles at thallus tips

Oarweed

Laminaria digitata (brown algae family)
H up to 150cm   thallophyte

The stalks of this seaweed expand when wet, and dried Oarweed sticks are used in obstetrics to dilate the cervix, e.g. to induce labour and in abortions. Alginic acid is indigestible and is used as a food additive and thickening agent, as well as in slimming aids. It soothes the stomach lining and is an ingredient in over-the-counter remedies for heartburn.

Habitat Rocky coastlines up to a water depth of 6m. Northern Atlantic and North Sea.

> attached to the rock via a root-like holdfast
> thallus yellow to olive or brown

holdfast

thallus fronds in digits

seaweed washed ashore

stem up to 4cm thick

stem with root-like holdfast

holdfast

245

Lungmoss

Lobaria pulmonaria (lichen)
H 10–40cm   thallophyte

Due to its resemblance to human lung tissue, this lichen was used in the past as a remedy for pulmonary complaints (Doctrine of Signatures). In addition, it was placed on wounds and ulcers and taken internally for bronchitis and catarrhs. These days it is used only in homeopathy, where it is still prescribed for coughs and catarrhs of the respiratory tract.

Habitat On the bark of trees, in mountain forests with high humidity. Northern hemisphere.

> broad, leafy thallus, with lobed edges
> underside pale and downy

turns grey during dry periods

surface ridged and pitted

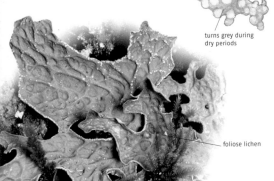

foliose lichen

Index of Species

Index of Species

Illustrations and Photographs

Illustrations
Golte-Bechtle/Kosmos (324); Haag/Kosmos (58); Hofmann/Kosmos (172); Kohnle/
Kosmos (121); Söllner/Kosmos (7); Spohn/Kosmos (113)

Photographs

Key
P = main photograph, H = habitat, M = margin, D = detail, b = bottom, t = top

Albers/Hecker 28H, 41H, 44tH, 47H, 57tH, 64tH, 102tH, 106P, 127bH, 134tH, 137bP, 139bH,
159H, 165H, 182H, 185bP, 188H, 204tP; Hassler 54tH, 60bH, 76tH, 79tH, 136bH; Hecker 18P, 18H,
19tP, 19bP, 19tH, 19bH, 21bP, 21bH, 22D, 23bP, 23bH, 24P, 24D, 25tP, 25bP, 25tH, 26P, 27bP, 27tH,
27bH, 28P, 29tP, 30P, 31tP, 31bP, 31bH, 32P, 32H, 33tP, 33bP, 33bH, 35bP, 35bH, 36P, 36H, 36D, 37P,
37H, 38bP, 39P, 40tP, 40bP, 40tH, 41P, 42tP, 43P, 44bP, 44bH, 45P, 45H, 46bP, 46bH, 47P, 48bH,
49P, 50P, 50H, 51tH, 52tP, 52tH, 52bH, 53P, 53H, 56P, 56H, 57tP, 59tP, 59tH, 60tH, 62P, 62H, 63H,
64bH, 65D, 66P, 66H, 67tP, 67bP, 67tH, 67bH, 68tP, 68tH, 69tP, 69bP, 69tH, 69bH, 70P, 70H,
71tH, 72tP, 72bH, 73P, 73H, 75P, 75H, 77tH, 78P, 79bP, 80P, 80H, 81tP, 81tH, 82P, 82H, 85P, 85H,
86bP, 87P, 90P, 90H, 91H, 92H, 93tP, 93tH, 93bH, 93tD, 96bP, 96bH, 97tP, 97tH, 98P, 98H,
99tP, 99bP, 99bH, 100tH, 101P, 101H, 102tP, 103bP, 103bH, 105bP, 107P, 107H, 108bP, 108tH,
108bH, 109P, 110P, 110H, 111bP, 111bH, 112P, 113tP, 113bP, 114P, 114H, 117tP, 117tH, 118tP, 118tH,
119P, 119H, 120tP, 121tP, 121tH, 122P, 122H, 123tP, 123bP, 123bH, 124tP, 125P, 125H, 129P, 129H,
130tP, 131bH, 137tP, 139bP, 140tP, 140bP, 140tH, 140bH, 142bH, 145tP, 145tH, 145bH, 147P, 147H,
148bP, 148bH, 149P, 151bP, 152H, 154P, 154H, 155bP, 156bP, 156bH, 157P, 157H, 158bP, 158bH, 160bP,
160bH, 161tP, 161bP, 161bH, 162P, 162H, 163P, 166bP, 166tH, 166bH, 167bP, 167bH, 168P, 168H,
168D, 169tP, 169bH, 172P, 173bP, 173tH, 173bH, 174tP, 174tH, 175P, 175H, 176tH, 177bP, 178H,
180bP, 183bP, 183bH, 184tP, 184bP, 185tP, 186P, 189P, 190bP, 190tH, 191bP, 191bH, 193bP, 193bH,
194P, 195tP, 195tH, 196P, 196H, 197tP, 197tH, 197bH, 198D, 198P, 198H, 199tP, 199bP, 199bH,
200P, 200H, 201P, 202tP, 202bP, 203bP, 203tH, 203bH, 204tH, 205bP, 206P, 206H, 207tP,
207bP, 208tH, 208bH, 209P, 209H, 210P, 210H, 212bP, 212bH, 213P, 213H, 214bP, 215P, 216P,
217tP, 217bP, 217bH, 218P, 219tP, 219tH, 221bP, 221bH, 222P, 222H, 223tP, 223bP, 224P, 225P, 226bD,
226tP, 226bP, 226tH, 226bH, 228P, 230bH, 234tP, 234tH, 235P, 236P, 236H, 238tP, 239P, 239H,
240H, 241tP, 241bP, 241bH, 242P, 242H, 243bH, 244H; **Helm/Hecker** 181H; König 20P, 21tP, 22P,
25bH, 29bH, 35tH, 48tH, 54bP, 72tH, 77bP, 77bH, 79bH, 83tP, 83tH, 84P, 84H, 86bH, 89H, 89H,
96tH, 105bH, 108tP, 113tH, 115tH, 115bP, 115H, 115bH, 118bH, 121bP, 128tH, 131H, 132bH, 139tH,
146bP, 153tP, 155bH, 158tP, 161tH, 164bH, 169tH, 174bP, 179tP, 180bH, 184bH, 188P, 194tH,
194bH, 204bH, 212tP, 214tP, 220H, 223bH, 229P, 230tH, 232tH, 233H, 234bH, 237bH, 238tH,
243bP, 245tH; **Lange/Hecker** 22H, 54bH; **Laux** 24H, 31tH, 40bH, 46tH, 57bH, 61bH, 88H, 112H,
116H, 124tH, 127H, 133H, 134tH, 137bH, 141H, 148tH, 151bH, 153H, 160tH, 164tH, 165P, 176bP, 181P,
182P, 183tD, 185tH, 187tP, 189H, 192H, 201H, 207tH, 211H, 218H, 221tH, 225H, 238bP, 245bP;
Mertz/Hecker 42tH, 124bH, 199tH, 215H; **Reinhard-Tierfoto, Hans Reinhard**
Heilgkreuzsteinach-Eiterbach 21tH, 42bH, 51bH, 86H, 135H, 151tH, 184H, 232bH;
Rühlemann 96tP; **Sauer/Hecker** 26H, 27tP, 29bP, 30H, 34P, 35tP, 44tP, 46tP, 48tP, 48bP, 50D,
52bP, 55P, 60tP, 61tP, 63P, 64bP, 65P, 68bP, 71tP, 72bP, 81bP, 83bP, 83bH, 89P, 89P, 91P, 92P, 93bP,
94P, 95P, 102bP, 103tP, 106H, 124bP, 126tP, 127bP, 128bP, 130bP, 133P, 135P, 136tP, 136bP, 142tP,
144P, 144H, 145bP, 148tP, 150bP, 150bH, 152P, 153bP, 155tP, 155tH, 159P, 163D, 164bP, 171tP, 174bH,
176tP, 177bH, 179bP, 180tP, 180tH, 190tP, 191tP, 192P, 194bP, 204bP, 208tP, 208bP, 219bH, 220P,
227tP, 227tD, 234bP, 240P, 244P, 245tP; **Schönfelder** 20H, 23tP, 23tH, 38tP, 51tP, 51bP, 54tP, 57bP,
59tH, 60bP, 61tH, 64tP, 69bD, 71bH, 74P, 74H, 76tP, 76bP, 76bH, 77tP, 79tP, 81bH, 88P, 94H,
97tP, 100tH, 100bP, 102bH, 104P, 105tP, 111tP, 120bP, 120tH, 120bH, 123tH, 127tP, 128tP, 130bH,
131bP, 132tP, 136tH, 138P, 138H, 139tP, 142bP, 142tH, 143P, 146bH, 149H, 150tP, 150tH, 153bH,

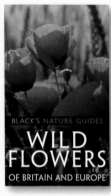

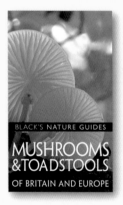